The Isaac Newton Telescope

The Isaac Newton Telescope

at Herstmonceux and on La Palma

Anthony Wilson

Science Projects Publishing

First published in Great Britain in 2010
by Science Projects Publishing

A CIP catalogue record for this title is available from the British Library

ISBN 978-0-9512394-2-1

Typeset in Adobe Garamond Pro from Adobe InDesign CS3

Printed and bound by Printondemand-worldwide, Peterborough, UK

the OBSERVATORY science centre

Science Projects Publishing, The Observatory Science Centre, Herstmonceux, HAILSHAM, BN27 1RN, UK
e-mail info@the-observatory.org   phone 01323 832731   fax 01323 832741
www.the-observatory.org

Cover:
Background image: some of the billions of stars in the outer reaches of the Andromeda galaxy (M31), imaged from La Palma in 2007 through blue and green filters with the Wide Field Camera on the Isaac Newton Telescope. (Narrow black bars on the original image arising from small gaps between CCD detectors have been artificially tinted here.)
Inset: The telescope at Herstmonceux.

Contents

Acknowledgements

This book has its origin in an event I witnessed in 2003. In the grounds of one of the former buildings of the Royal Greenwich Observatory at Herstmonceux in Sussex, a large wooden crate which had lain there for some months was finally prised open. Inside was an enormous piece of Pyrex – a disc six feet in diameter, a foot thick, and weighing more than four tons. It is the life-story of this disc and the telescope of which it was once a part, that is related in these pages. My first thanks therefore go to Steve Pizzey and his colleagues at Science Projects, whose vision and enterprise brought part of the Observatory back to life as a Science Centre and secured the return of the giant Pyrex disc for display there.

Among the many people who helped in various ways as I researched the book I am particularly indebted to Adam Perkins, whose responsibilities at Cambridge University Library include the very extensive RGO Archives, to Javier Méndez Alvarez, my enthusiastic and welcoming guide at the La Palma observatory, and to my wife Margaret, for her continuing support and encouragement. My thanks also go to Angela Welling who opened up the disused dome at Herstmonceux for me, to David Brooks who showed me the optical polishing equipment at UCL, and more generally to the staff of Cambridge University Library, the Royal Society Library and the National Archives. I am grateful also to the people and organisations named on page 144 who provided pictures.

My task was made easier by the availability of two first-rate websites: the Astrophysics Data System site (www.adsabs.harvard. edu) which allows free and instant downloading of full-text scans of much of the astronomical literature, including historical material, and the comprehensive and informative Isaac Newton Group site (http://www.ing.iac.es/) run by Javier Méndez Alvarez.

Finally, I am especially grateful to the former RGO astronomers Paul Murdin and Roger Wood, who read the book in proof, and to Chris Benn, formerly of the RGO and now Head of Astronomy for the Isaac Newton Group, who checked the La Palma chapters. In addition to spotting a number of significant errors, they provided helpful comments and suggestions, all of which I have adopted.

Anthony Wilson
intbook@btinternet.com

Chronology

Abbreviations

CCD   Charge-Coupled Device
CCI   International Scientific Committee
ENO   European Northern Observatory
GMT   Greenwich Mean Time
IAC   Astronomical Institute of the Canary Islands
IDS   Intermediate Dispersion Spectrograph
IGC   Inter-government Convention
IIA   Inter-institution Agreement
ING   Isaac Newton Group
INT   Isaac Newton Telescope
IPCS   Image Photon Counting System
IPHAS   INT Photometric Hydrogen Alpha Survey
JKT   Jacobus Kapteyn Telescope
MPBW   Ministry of Public Building and Works
NGC   New General Catalogue
NHO   Northern Hemisphere Observatory
NHRC   Northern Hemisphere Review Committee
NIA   National Institute for Astronomy
ORM   Observatorio del Roque de los Muchachos
RAS   Royal Astronomical Society
RGO   Royal Greenwich Observatory
ROE   Royal Observatory, Edinburgh
SCP   Supernova cosmology project
SRC   Science Research Council
WASP   Wide Angle Search for Planets
WFC   Wide Field Camera
WHT   William Herschel Telescope

Introduction

THE 1066 WALK is a long-distance path that meanders through the Sussex countryside near the south coast of England. At one point it passes the roman walls of Pevensey Castle, and at another runs close to the site of the Battle of Hastings. Between the two, near the mediaeval castle of Herstmonceux, there is a historic monument of a totally different kind. On private land a few yards from the path, a windowless cylindrical building, domed at the top, stands higher than the surrounding trees. Nowadays it is locked and abandoned, but in December 1967 the Queen came here to inaugurate the Isaac Newton Telescope, the largest in the world outside America and Russia, and intended to be 'the greatest single contribution to the development of observational astronomy ever made in this country'.[1] How such a large instrument came to be constructed in Britain, what it was used for, and why it is no longer here, is a long and tortuous tale – so long and tortuous in fact that officials of the government department which had to foot the bills came to know it simply as 'that damned telescope'.[2]

The original Isaac Newton dome stands empty in Sussex ...

Two thousand miles away, on a rugged mountaintop in the Canary islands, another dome stands among several others, visible to passing trekkers. Inside is the telescope that was once at Herstmonceux, adapted and improved but basically the same instrument, and now benefiting from the 'serene and quiet air' which Isaac Newton himself predicted would be found 'above the grosser clouds'.[3] How the 'damned telescope' was moved to the tropics, was re-inaugurated there by the Duke of Gloucester, and enjoys a successful second life, forms part two of our story.

...while the telescope operates at its new high-level home in the Canary Islands.

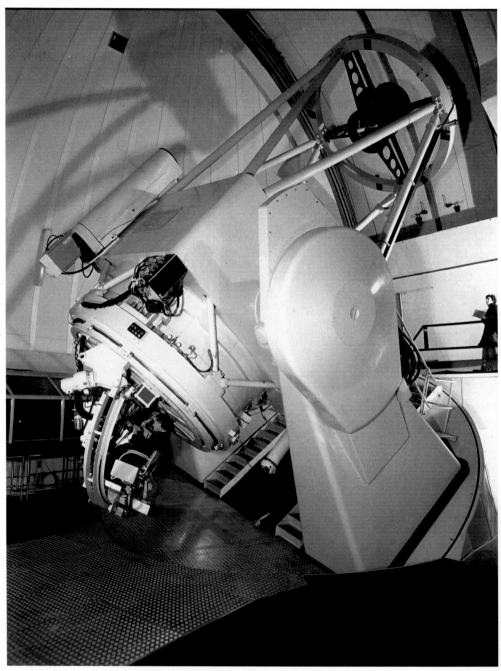

The Isaac Newton Telescope in its dome at Herstmonceux in 1974.

Part One

'That Damned Telescope'

THE TELESCOPE AT HERSTMONCEUX

The Isaac Newton dome has been a landmark on the Sussex skyline since the 1960s.

Celebrating Sir Isaac I

IN OCTOBER 1944 the Second World War was in its fifth year and London and southeast England were still under daily attack from Hitler's flying bombs and missiles. Nevertheless it was in that month that a committee was set up to plan for the future needs of astronomy in Britain – reflecting the general perception that the tide of war had turned and victory would not be long in coming. The war had of course seriously disrupted activities, with practically every astronomer in the country engaged in war work for up to six years, but there was a much deeper malaise to be addressed. Observational astronomy in Britain had been in decline for decades, to the extent that the mid-1940s were described as the Dark Age of professional astronomy here. A survey in 1945 would reveal that the total number of higher posts for professional astronomers at UK observatories was only fifteen – fewer than the number of senior posts at just one of the large American observatories. And with postgraduate instruction at a standstill during the war, there was no new cadre of trained, though inexperienced, astronomers waiting in the wings.

In 1944 there was no larger telescope in Britain than the 36-inch 'Yapp' reflector at Greenwich, shown here after its move to Herstmonceux. Its light-gathering power was one eighth that of the largest American telescope.

Central to the problem was a lack of good telescopes. Most of the instruments at British observatories were old, several of them dating from the 1880s and none larger than a 36-inch (this being the diameter of the main mirror in the country's largest telescopes – smaller, in fact, than one built by William Herschel in the 1780s). Germany, Italy, the USSR, Sweden, Switzerland, France, Belgium, the USA and Canada all had larger instruments.[1] In theoretical astronomy – the sort where a telescope is not necessary – Britain was still a force to be reckoned with, but in observational work the country that had once been a world leader now lagged far behind. Supremacy in observational astronomy had passed to the United

States in the early twentieth century. Alone among those industrial countries able to support professional astronomy, the USA had both ample finance, from a new breed of successful industrialists turning to philanthropy, and fine observing sites in the clear and steady air of its western mountaintops. The 100-inch Hooker telescope in California had been the world's largest since 1917.

The 100-inch Hooker reflector at Mount Wilson in California, dating from 1917, was still the world's largest telescope in the early 1940s. It is still in operation but narrowly escaped destruction by fire in 2009.

In contrast to the professional situation, it is worth mentioning that among the general public in Britain interest in astronomy remained high. Wartime blackout regulations had cut down light pollution, while volunteers in the Observer Corps had had plenty of time to study the night sky as they watched for enemy aircraft. Amateur astronomers, often owning their own telescopes, had increased in number and activity and were making a valuable contribution to the study of the planets, meteors and other night sky objects.

The initiative that would eventually lead to the construction of a large new British telescope came from two learned societies, and two eminent astronomers. The Royal Society, founded in 1661, was, and is, the most prestigious academy of leading scientists. To be elected a Fellow of the Royal Society is the highest distinction available to a scientist in the UK apart from receiving the Nobel Prize. The Society's aim is to foster excellence in all branches of scientific research. Making sure that scientists have access to the necessary research tools, such as telescopes, is part of its brief, and until the 1960s it was able to obtain money direct from the Treasury for major research projects. In the 1940s the premises of the Royal Society were in Burlington House, off Piccadilly in London. Also in Burlington House were, and are, the premises of a second learned society, the Royal Astronomical Society (RAS), founded in 1820. It is the country's leading professional organisation for scientists working in astronomy and allied fields. Both societies were to play an important part in promoting the idea of a new large telescope for Britain.

Among the many individuals who advanced the idea of the telescope and helped persuade government to fund it, two names stand out: H. H. Plaskett, Professor of Astronomy at Oxford, and Sir Harold Spencer Jones, the Astronomer Royal. Harry Plaskett was a Canadian who took up the astronomy chair at Oxford in 1932 and immediately set about revitalising the moribund observatory there. He was primarily a researcher whose main interest was the sun. He built two solar telescopes at Oxford to analyse the sun's light by the techniques of spectroscopy (studying spectral lines) and photometry (measuring their brightness). In recognition of his lifetime's work, and that of his father, also an eminent astronomer, one of the asteroids was named Plaskett in 1984. But it was as president of the Royal Astronomical Society from 1945-47 that he became the leading advocate for the new telescope.

As Astronomer Royal, Harold Spencer Jones was head of the Royal Observatory at Greenwich from 1933 to 1955, only the tenth person to hold the post in more than 250 years. He was an astronomer of worldwide repute, notable for co-ordinating a complex international effort to measure the scale of the solar system by observing the minor planet Eros. He also showed that the Earth's rotation has irregularities that make it unsuitable for use as a precise timekeeper, leading eventually to the adoption of atomic time as the standard. As Astronomer Royal Spencer Jones would lead the Royal Observatory into the most momentous event in its three hundred year history, its removal to a new site. In the late 1930s he had begun to look for somewhere where observing conditions would be better than at Greenwich, which by then had been enveloped by the growth of London with its attendant smoke and light pollution. But the Second World War intervened and it was not until 1945 that a country site, at Herstmonceux in Sussex, was adopted as the observatory's new home.

Harold Spencer Jones was the Astronomer Royal who moved the Royal Observatory from Greenwich to Herstmonceux. He played a major part in initiating the INT project.

The planning committee set up by the Royal Society in October 1944 had Spencer Jones as chairman and Plaskett as a member, but did not in fact meet until the following July, by which time peace had been declared in Europe. Two months later it submitted a draft Report on the Post-War Needs in Astronomy, and it is in this document that we read the first tentative suggestion for a new telescope. After expressing doubts about the suitability of the British climate for 'instruments of the largest size', the Committee 'considered, however, that a reflector of 60-inch aperture at a selected site in southeast England could be effectively used'[2]. (A reflector is a telescope whose main optical component is a concave mirror.) The committee's report seems to have been mislaid, however, and was not considered by the Council of the Royal Society until March of the following year. In the meantime the Royal Astronomical Society had seized the initiative.

The RAS held regular meetings on Friday afternoons at its headquarters in Burlington House. The meeting on 8th February 1946 was a special occasion, and would come to be seen as a historic one too. After discussing the appearance that week of possibly the largest sunspot ever photographed from Greenwich, and rewarding one of its members with a medal for his research into magnetic storms, the meeting came to its main business. This was the Presidential Address, given by Professor Plaskett and bearing the innocent title of 'Astronomical Telescopes'[3]. In it Plaskett appealed eloquently for the revival of British observational astronomy. 'The future progress of astronomy in Great Britain', he argued, 'depends on the construction of at least one large telescope'. His own preference was for a reflector of about 74-inch aperture. Even allowing for the British climate, there were plenty of research topics such an instrument could be effectively used for. He went on to outline his own view of what sort of telescope the new one should be, and even gave an estimate of what it might cost. Significantly, in view of what was to follow, he said nothing about how, or by whom, the business of actually getting it built was to be handled.

Plaskett's address galvanised the RAS. So enthusiastically was his proposal received that the two secretaries of the society, Donald Sadler and William McCrea, met together the very next morning to plan how to get the Society's Council moving on the matter. (Saturday half-day working was still the norm at that time). Meetings were held in the following weeks to flesh out the proposal, and on 14th May the RAS made formal application to the Royal Society for 'a sum of the order of £100,000 to build a reflecting telescope of at least 72 inches aperture, together with its dome, for observational astronomy in the United Kingdom'[4]. By now the telescope had acquired two important features: it had a possible home, and it had a name.

Herstmonceux Castle, with its surrounding estate, became the new home of the Royal Observatory in 1946.

The new instrument was to be sited in southern England and one location had obvious advantages. The Herstmonceux estate, centred round a mediaeval castle seven miles from Eastbourne on the Sussex coast, had been chosen after much careful research as the new site for the Royal Observatory when it moved from Greenwich. It offered, according to Spencer Jones, 'about the best conditions available in this country'[5]. By April 1946 the Admiralty, which had responsibility for the observatory, had negotiated the purchase of the estate, and since it encompassed 368 acres there would be no difficulty in accommodating the new telescope there too. It was also proposed that the telescope would come under the administrative direction of the Astronomer Royal, so it made sense to site it with the Royal Observatory, even though the telescope itself was not to be part of that institution.

In June 1946 the RAS held an extra meeting to discuss how to make use of the large telescope for which they were seeking funds. First on the agenda was a report from the Astronomer Royal, presented by his Chief Assistant, Robert Atkinson, on the crucial issue of the observing conditions to be expected at Herstmonceux.[6] It was designed to dispel any doubts about the wisdom of siting a large telescope there by calculating how much clear night sky could be expected. No-one had measured this directly, but daytime figures were available. Over the period from 1901 to 1930 the sun had shone at Herstmonceux for 40 per cent of the time it was above the horizon. Data from Greenwich, where figures for night-time clear sky as well as daytime sunshine were available, showed that the number of clear hours at night was slightly greater than the number of sunshine hours by day, and the same was expected to be true at Herstmonceux. The upshot was that there should be about 1,500 hours of clear sky there per year, when the new telescope could be put to good use. This was actually more than the number of hours available at Canada's Dominion Observatory in Victoria, where the existing 72-inch telescope was producing 'magnificent results'. Since every hour that an astronomer spent at the telescope was reckoned to lead to anything between eight and several hundred hours away from it analysing the results, 1,500 hours observing a year would be enough to keep a 'considerable number' of astronomers in full-time occupation. There is no evidence in the published report of this meeting that anyone demurred from the conclusion that Herstmonceux would be an adequate site for the new telescope.

Isaac Newton, from a bust at the Royal Observatory, Greenwich.

Plans were well advanced by the spring of 1946 for a week-long celebration, to be held in July that year, to mark the tercentenary of the birth of the man generally regarded as Britain's greatest scientist, Sir Isaac Newton. (Newton was actually born in 1642, but in 1942 the country had been too deeply involved in the war to hold more than the most muted commemoration.) Helping to plan the 1946 anniversary event was the mathematician and geophysicist Professor Sydney Chapman, and it was he, along with the astrophysicist William McCrea who made the inspired suggestion that the new telescope could be linked to the tercentenary. The idea found favour and the project was christened the Newton Memorial Observatory. Eventually, when it became clear that the new observatory would consist of the one telescope only, it became known simply as the Isaac Newton Telescope (INT), a name it has held ever since. What made the connection particularly appropriate was the fact that it was Newton himself who invented one type of reflecting telescope and made the first example of it.

Linking the telescope to the Newton anniversary was a masterstroke, for in addition to providing a name it also set a deadline. The fact that the Tercentenary Celebrations were due to start in mid-July was a spur to action, both for those who had to apply for funding and for those with the power to grant it. The RAS's 14th May proposal was welcomed by the Royal Society Committee on the Post-War Needs in Astronomy, and a modified version of it was placed at the top of a list of priorities. The Committee still favoured a 72-inch telescope, while pointing out that a 100-inch instrument would be even better. Since the light-collecting power of a telescope depends on the surface area of its main mirror, this increase in diameter would nearly double the light-gathering power of the instrument. This would mean that photographs of faint objects would require a shorter exposure time – important at a site where many nights would be only intermittently clear. But at an estimated £200,000, including the building and dome to house it, the larger telescope might be too expensive. In the event the Royal Society resolved in mid-June to apply to the Treasury for about £150,000 for the Isaac Newton project, a sum equivalent to nearly four million pounds today.

The senior Treasury official who dealt with the request, Sir Alan Barlow, was concerned about some of the details, but supportive in principle. It helped that the prestige of science had never stood higher, following the crucial contribution scientists and engineers had made to winning the war.

Barlow was a most unusual civil servant. A baronet, a notable collector of Islamic pottery and Chinese ceramics, and married to a granddaughter of Charles Darwin, he carried out much of his official business not from the Treasury but from the rooms of various London clubs. Seeking reassurance about the ownership and management of the telescope, he summoned Spencer Jones to a meeting. When this took place the Astronomer Royal's case proved so persuasive that Barlow agreed to advise the Chancellor of the Exchequer that money should be made available not for the 72-inch telescope originally requested, but for the even larger 100-inch one.

In just four weeks news came through that the Chancellor, Hugh Dalton, had agreed in principle to ask parliament to vote the necessary funds. Three days later, the Newton Tercentenary Meeting began. The celebrations were attended by delegates from 36 nations and included a garden party hosted by the King and Queen at Buckingham Palace. (Among the guests was the 88 year-old Professor Max Planck, founder of quantum theory. Planck was German by birth, but was poignantly announced at the Meeting as the representative of 'no country'. One of his sons had been executed by the Nazis two years earlier, and the old man's home destroyed by allied bombing.)

The President of the Royal Society at this time was Sir Robert Robinson, soon to be awarded the Nobel Prize for his investigations in organic chemistry. At the opening session at Burlington House on 15th July 1946, Sir Robert made the first public announcement that Britain was to have what he called an 'Isaac Newton Observatory', to house a reflecting telescope of 100 inches aperture, as a National Memorial to commemorate the tercentenary of the birth of the greatest British man of science.

When Parliament duly voted the funds, the Royal Astronomical Society's initiative reached its triumphant culmination. The bid had benefited from the unique influence and authority of the Royal Society, and the support of the Astronomer Royal, whose 'powerful advocacy', in the words of one of the Secretaries of the RAS, 'met with an immediate reward such as can but rarely, if ever, have been achieved by anyone making a submission to H. M. Treasury'[7]. Sadly, Spencer Jones would not live to see the commencement, let alone the completion, of the construction of the telescope at Herstmonceux. But he and Plaskett should be remembered as joint founding fathers of the Isaac Newton Telescope, and prime instigators of a postwar resurgence in observational astronomy in Britain.

The decision to build the Isaac Newton Telescope, taken so soon after the end of a debilitating war, was bold and forward-looking. Yet even as the cheering died away, the seeds of future controversy had been sown. Plaskett's original proposal had been for a complex type of telescope of untried design, an idea that would resurface later and engender much debate and delay. The decision to site so powerful an instrument under English skies would be repeatedly questioned in the years ahead. One correspondent to *The Times* would eventually call it a 'disgraceful waste of public money'[8].

Design by committee 2

THE ISAAC NEWTON TELESCOPE, as announced on that summer day in 1946, would be equal in size to the largest telescope operating anywhere in the world at that time. This was the 100-inch Hooker telescope at Mount Wilson Observatory in California with which Edwin Hubble had discovered the expansion of the universe. But the INT was not the first venture into heroic telescope-building in Britain.

William Herschel's 40-foot telescope caused a sensation in 1789 but was too unwieldy to do much useful astronomy.

In 1789 William Herschel completed what was then the world's largest telescope – larger in fact than any telescope operating in Britain today. Its tube was 40 feet long and its main component a metal mirror 48 inches in diameter and weighing nearly a ton. It became the wonder of the age and visitors, from the Royal Family downwards, came from far and wide to Herschel's home in Slough to marvel at it. Herschel was the leading astronomer of his time, and a telescope-builder *par excellence*. He constructed many fine instruments, but the 48-inch was not one of them. It was too unwieldy for convenient use. Valuable observing time was spent preparing it for use, and two assistants had to be on hand. Herschel did discover two hitherto unknown satellites of Saturn with this telescope, but preferred to use smaller instruments for most of his continuing astronomical work. The 48-inch was eventually dismantled. One of its mirrors is now on show in the Science

Museum in London, while part of the iron tube – wide enough for King George III to have walked through it – is displayed at the old Royal Observatory in Greenwich.

The nineteenth century saw the construction of an even more remarkable telescope, known as the Leviathan of Parsonstown. This was a 72-inch reflector set up in the 1840s by William Parsons, third Earl of Rosse, on his estate in central Ireland. Like Herschel's 48-inch it had a metal primary mirror. Two of these, each weighing about four tons, were cast on site, and then ground and polished to the correct concave shape by the Earl and his staff. Despite its immense size – the tube was 58 feet long – and the fact that its mounting did not allow it to point to all parts of the sky, the telescope did much useful work. Its huge light-gathering power enabled observers to see objects that were much fainter and more distant than any seen before. In particular certain nebulae which only appeared as faint fuzzy patches in other telescopes were shown to have a distinct spiral structure (see page 141 for an example). The Leviathan was the world's largest telescope for more than sixty years, but went out of use in the early twentieth century. It has recently been restored and can be visited at Birr Castle. One of its original mirrors is now held by the Science Museum in London.

The 72-inch Rosse telescope, the 'Leviathan of Parsonstown'.

A third venture into large telescope building was the construction of a 60-inch reflector in the 1880s by the leading amateur astronomer Dr Andrew Common. This had a glass mirror, coated on its front surface with a layer of silver applied by a chemical process. The telescope was set up at Common's home in

Ealing, but was little used, partly because London had expanded so much that the night sky over Ealing was no longer very dark. It was sold to an American observatory in 1904 and eventually moved to South Africa. With a new primary mirror and many other improvements it is still in service there.

These three telescopes all enjoyed one advantage that the Isaac Newton Telescope was to lack: each was brought to completion by the zeal, determination and skill of a single individual. Herschel, Parsons, and Common personally supplied the driving force, decision-making and expertise that went into the construction of these instruments. Design and construction of the INT, on the other hand, would be in the hands of committees.

Responsibility for the design of the INT and the supervision of its construction had been vested in a Board of Management, which held its first meeting in July 1947, a year after funding had been announced. The Board's membership was drawn from the great and good of the scientific world: four Directors of Observatories, four Fellows of the Royal Society, and four Fellows of the Royal Astronomical Society. Among them were four Professors, three Knights and one Lord (Lord Cherwell, who had been Churchill's principal scientific adviser during the War). Spencer Jones, as Astronomer Royal, was to take the chair at Board meetings. All were busy men, Spencer Jones, who was to have 'administrative control' of the telescope, perhaps the busiest of all. From the outset, then, decision-making was to be by consensus. In addition to the lack of an obvious driving-force for the project, there was inevitably also a lack of experience in building and using large telescopes. As already mentioned, the only other 100-inch telescope in the world was in America, and had been constructed thirty years earlier (though the 200-inch Hale instrument at Mount Palomar in California was nearing completion).

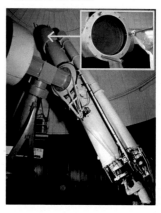

The Thompson 26-inch telescope at Herstmonceux is an example of a refractor. Its primary component is a lens, shown in the inset.

Early meetings of the INT's Board of Management were dominated by a single question: just what sort of telescope was it to be? Construction could not begin until this question was answered. In the event, reaching a firm and final decision on this issue would take nine years of investigation and debate, and would not be concluded before a new Astronomer Royal was in post.

That the INT would be some type of *reflecting* telescope, using a large concave mirror to collect and focus starlight, was a foregone conclusion. In the alternative type, the *refracting* telescope, a converging lens similar to a large magnifying glass is used to collect and focus light, and there is a practical limit to how large such a lens can be. A very large lens is thick and heavy. Above a certain size it is not possible to achieve the required degree of clarity and freedom from flaws in the glass of such a lens. Also glass, like all materials, cannot be made infinitely rigid. This means that a heavy

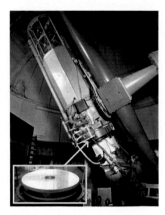

RGO astronomer Paul Murdin with the Yapp 36-inch telescope at Herstmonceux. The Yapp is a reflector; its primary component is a mirror, shown in the inset.

lens is liable to sag under its own weight, so that its shape will be slightly different when it is horizontal, compared to when it is on edge. Thus the optical properties of the lens would vary according to where in the sky the telescope is pointed, and this limits its usefulness. There are also problems in any lens telescope due to the fact that glass refracts light of different colours by differing amounts, producing an effect known as chromatic aberration.

The largest refractor ever made has a lens 40 inches in diameter, well below the 100 inches planned for the INT. It was built in 1897 and is at the Yerkes Observatory in Wisconsin, USA. In Britain the largest are the 28-inch refractor at Greenwich and the 26-inch Thompson refractor at Herstmonceux. Both date from the late nineteenth century when there was a vogue for this type of instrument. Refractors such as these have their uses, particularly for very precise measurement of the positions of objects in the sky. But their comparatively small aperture limits the amount of light they can catch, making them unsuitable for the study of extremely faint and distant objects.

Using a mirror in place of the large lens removes some of these difficulties. Astronomical mirrors carry their reflecting surface on the front, unlike mirrors at home which have the silvering behind the glass. This means that light never actually enters the glass of a telescope mirror, so it is not a problem if this glass has flaws in it, so long as they do not affect the front surface. There is also no chromatic aberration with a mirror, although other forms of optical difficulty can arise. Unlike a lens which can only be held round its edge, a mirror can be supported on the back, minimizing difficulties caused by the mirror changing shape under its own weight when it is tilted. All the largest modern telescopes are reflectors. But what sort of reflecting telescope should the Isaac Newton be?

All reflectors have their main concave (bowl-shaped) mirror – the primary – at the foot, facing up the tube, but there are several options for how the rest of the instrument is arranged. In the type of telescope that Newton himself devised a smaller flat mirror – the secondary – is placed at 45 degrees near the top of the tube, and the observer looks in from the side, using an eyepiece to magnify the image. Newton's pioneering reflectors were small, with apertures of only an inch or two, and their mirrors were cast in metal and shaped and polished by Newton himself. He used an alloy of copper and tin known as speculum metal, which has the advantage that it can be given a good reflecting surface, and the disadvantages that it is brittle and also tarnishes quickly, needing frequent repolishing. Metal mirrors remained the norm until the mid-nineteenth century when the technique of coating a glass surface with a thin layer of silver to make a mirror was developed. A reflecting telescope believed to incorporate parts of the one

Isaac Newton's original telescope: a replica constructed in the workshops at Herstmonceux.

made by Newton in the winter of 1671-2 is kept today at the Royal Society.

Newtonian reflectors are popular with amateur astronomers, but the larger instruments used by professionals are seldom of this type. Instead, a number of other arrangements are used, as shown below. The simplest is the prime focus set-up in which the primary mirror focuses an image directly onto a detector mounted inside the telescope near the top. A second type of reflector is the Cassegrain, developed in France a few years after Newton's invention. Here there is a secondary, convex, mirror which reflects light back down the tube. The eyepiece or other detector is at the bottom, viewing through a central hole in the primary mirror. As with the Newtonian design, the secondary mirror blocks out a small percentage of the light that would otherwise be collected by the telescope, but does not produce a hole in the image seen by the observer. Newton himself was scornful of the Cassegrain design, saying it had no advantages and many disadvantages and would never be put into practice. But he was wrong; Cassegrain telescopes are compact and in large sizes the observing position at the lower end makes them convenient to use. They soon became popular, and remain so today.

A third type of reflector, the Gregorian, was actually the first to be put forward, by the Scottish mathematician James Gregory in 1663. The design is similar to the Cassegrain, except that the secondary mirror is further away from the primary, and is concave rather than convex.

The quality of the image seen through these telescopes depends crucially on the precise shape of the concave surface of the primary mirror. In simple Newtonian, Cassegrain and Gregorian telescopes this follows the mathematical form known as a paraboloid – the shape of a satellite dish. With a paraboloidal mirror the telescope produces an image that is sharp at the centre but less good towards the edges. A central star appears as a sharp point of light, but stars near the edge are distorted into comet-like smudges, a defect known as coma. To overcome this problem a new type of wide-

Optical arrangement of a Newtonian reflector.

Optical arrangement of various types of reflecting telescope, set up for photographic use. The first three are also suitable for visual use by replacing the photographic plate with an eyepiece .

M – primary mirror,
S – secondary mirror,
P – photographic plate
C – corrector plate.

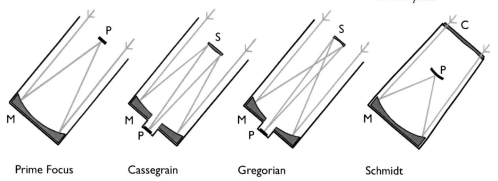

Prime Focus   Cassegrain   Gregorian   Schmidt

field telescope was devised by the Estonian astronomer Bernhard Schmidt in the 1930s.

In a Schmidt telescope the primary mirror is not paraboloidal but spherical in shape, like the inside of a ball. As shown on the previous page, light enters the telescope through a special lens of complex shape called a corrector plate, and is focused onto a photographic plate or other detector mounted inside the telescope. Schmidts are generally used for survey work, in which large areas of sky are imaged, rather than for the study of individual small objects.

A crucial factor in choosing what type of telescope to build was a consideration of how the Isaac Newton Telescope would be used. Astronomers such as Herschel and the Earl of Rosse simply looked through their telescopes and drew what they saw. But by the 1940s this direct approach had long been abandoned, at least amongst most professional astronomers. Two new techniques, photography and spectroscopy, began to be applied to astronomy in the late nineteenth century and became the principal observing methods used with larger telescopes throughout most of the twentieth, until digital techniques eventually took over.

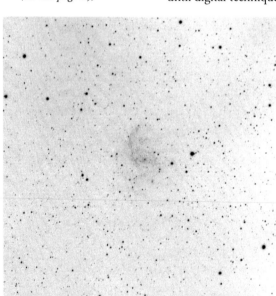

Example of an astrophotograph, part of a plate exposed on the 26-inch refractor at Herstmonceux in 1981. The area covered is roughly equal to that of the full moon. The dots are individual stars and a spiral galaxy (NGC6946) is faintly visible at the centre. (See also page 119)

To use a telescope as a camera it was simply necessary to replace the eyepiece with a photographic plate – a glass sheet with a photosensitive coating, similar to that on black-and-white camera film. Because the objects being photographed were so faint, time exposures ranging up to several hours were used, gathering enough light to reveal sights that are much too faint to be seen with the naked eye. When the photographic plate was developed, a permanent image was obtained which could be measured and studied later, and preserved for future reference. The complete archive of photographs taken on the telescopes of the Royal Observatory between 1888 and 1988, for example, is held in a secure store in London and runs to some 120,000 plates, weighing 18 tons – a permanent record of a century of observing at Greenwich and Herstmonceux.

Astrophotography, as the technique is called, placed new demands on the designers and operators of telescopes. Even the largest and heaviest telescopes had to be precision scientific instruments. Careful optical design and high quality components were needed in order to minimize distortion and blurring in the image, particularly near the edges of the plate. Telescopes had to be manoeuvrable with great precision, to aim accurately at targets in the sky. In addition, since the Earth is rotating, the target appears to move across the sky during the course of a time exposure, and the telescope must precisely track this movement. The slightest error or unevenness in the tracking motion leads to blurring of the image.

In 1666 Isaac Newton passed a beam of sunlight through a triangular glass prism and produced a spectrum – an artificial rainbow – on a screen nearby. He showed that white light is a mixture of all the colours of the rainbow and that the prism, by deflecting different colours by different amounts, was sorting white light into its component colours. More than two centuries later astronomers began to apply the same technique to the light from individual stars. By training a telescope on to a particular star and passing the light it collected through a prism it was possible to capture the faint spectrum of the star on a photographic plate.

Example of a stellar spectrum, obtained with the 36-inch reflector at Herstmonceux in 1960. The broad black bar is the star's spectrum. The 'bar-codes' above and below it are spectra of a known light source, added for reference when the original spectrum was taken.

A new branch of science, astrophysics, was born – the study of the intrinsic properties of the stars and other objects in the universe. Spectroscopes began to be attached to many telescopes and as techniques developed, a wealth of information was obtained. Detailed analysis of a stellar spectrum can provide data about the atoms and molecules that are emitting light in the star, about the temperature of the star's surface, and, through the Doppler effect, about the speed at which the star is moving towards or away from the Earth. Spectroscopy became the key research tool of astronomers in the twentieth century, and remains so today. It relies on large telescopes to gather enough light to produce a detectable spectrum from faint and distant objects.

Even before funding was assured for the Isaac Newton Telescope, astronomers were discussing the research topics they might use it for. At a meeting of the Royal Astronomical Society in June 1946 Professor William Greaves was asked to speak about possible programmes of observation with a large telescope in Britain[1]. He was Astronomer Royal for Scotland, a professor at Edinburgh university, and a respected elder statesman of British astronomy.

Greaves identified three particular areas of interest, of which the first concerned the size, shape and structure of our galaxy. Astronomers had long suspected that the sun – a typical star – was a member of a vast swarm of stars which has come to be known as the Milky Way galaxy. Attempts had been made to determine the scale and structure of the galaxy, but the task was made more difficult by the fact that we are embedded within the galaxy and cannot see it from outside, and by the presence of clouds of dust and gas which block out our view of much of it. The proposed new telescope could help to build up a picture of the galaxy, Greaves argued, by providing good measurements of the brightness of large numbers of faint stars in all parts of the sky. To do this, a powerful instrument of the Schmidt type would be the preferred design.

Greaves' second area of interest was in the study of individual stars. Here the greater light-gathering power of the Isaac Newton Telescope would bring a huge increase in productivity. The spectrum of a faint star could be photographed in less than a tenth of the time it took with existing telescopes, where exposures up to three hours in duration were sometimes needed. If the new telescope were of conventional type, such as a Cassegrain, with a suitable spectroscope attached, fainter stars could be studied than was currently possible. Much more data would be obtained and the science of astrophysics would progress more rapidly.

Finally the Isaac Newton Telescope would allow British astronomers access to an area of discovery at one of the most exciting frontiers of modern science, the study of the universe on the largest scale, known as cosmology. Ever since the time of William Herschel astronomers had been aware of numerous faint nebulae – small fuzzy patches – in the sky, but only in the twentieth century had it become generally agreed that many of these – the faint spiral objects that the Earl of Rosse had identified with his Leviathan – were in fact individual galaxies, similar to, but immensely remote from, our own Milky Way galaxy. If the new telescope were a wide-aperture Schmidt, according to Greaves, capable of measuring the brightness of large numbers of these faint external galaxies, then an effective British contribution to this major new area of astronomy would be possible. A million galaxies could be within its range.

The problem with Greaves' proposals was that no one telescope could do it all. Some research projects would require a large telescope of conventional design, while others needed a wide-angle instrument of the Schmidt type. Each option had its own supporters and it was clear that what British astronomy really needed was not one new telescope, but two. It was thought that funding would not stretch that far, however, and a radical alternative began to gain ground. Perhaps, as Harry Plaskett had proposed in his original 1946 address to the RAS, the Isaac Newton could be the world's first large *dual-purpose* telescope. Some of the time it would operate as a wide-angle instrument, and then, with a few hours work replacing some of the optical components, it would become a conventional telescope, specially suitable for spectroscopy. That way the astronomers could have their cake and eat it.

Building a dual-purpose telescope would be a tough challenge.

Optical components would have to be positioned to extremely high precision, and no structure then known would prevent them moving slightly as the telescope's weight caused it to distort when it was tilted to view a new part of the sky. Another drawback was the telescope's length, which would be 50 feet for the dual instrument.

The danger was that the telescope would end up doing both jobs badly. Nevertheless, as so often with committees, it was the compromise that was adopted by the Board of Management; the INT would be a dual-purpose telescope. Basically it would be by far the world's most powerful Schmidt camera, with its primary mirror given a spherical shape and a corrector plate mounted at the top end. It would be convertible to a form of Gregorian telescope by removing the corrector plate and inserting a specially-shaped secondary mirror inside the tube. In this configuration it would be used for spectroscopy. As a Schmidt camera it would serve for direct photography over an area of sky 3.5 degrees wide – seven times the width of the full moon.

No telescope like this had ever been made before. The Isaac Newton Telescope would be an instrument of advanced design, pushing forward the frontiers of telescope technology. It would show the world what Britain could do. To harness the range of expertise this ambition demanded, the Board of Management set up a number of committees, and brought in experts to serve on them. By 1949 there were no fewer than five such committees, each with a brief to advise the Board on a specific aspect of the telescope's design. The functions of the Committee on Optical Design and the Committee on Mechanical Design are self-evident. Two further committees, on Servo Controls and on Photoelectric guiding, were concerned with how the telescope might be manoeuvred to the required degree of precision and how it would track objects as the Earth rotated. Finally there was a Committee on Spectroscope Design.

The Board's decision to build a dual-purpose instrument, taken finally in June 1949, would delay the construction of the INT by several years. It assumed, rashly, that a solution could be found to the problem of the telescope bending when it was tilted. There were also uncertainties about how the whole telescope would be mounted. In the end, these problems would prove insurmountable. Eventually, after years of fruitless research and design work, the dual-purpose design would have to be abandoned.

3 A gift from America

Whatever the eventual outcome of the deliberations of the design committees, one thing was certain from the start: the telescope would need a large concave mirror. With a diameter of more than eight feet, it would be the primary optical component of the INT. A microscopically thin layer of shiny metal coated on to its surface would catch light from the sky and bring it to a focus.

In the early twentieth century, telescope mirrors were usually made from normal plate glass. This had one important drawback: its sensitivity to changing temperature. Like most materials, glass expands slightly when warmed and contracts when cooled. For a telescope mirror this can lead to trouble if the mirror warms or cools in a non-uniform way, so that one part of it, such as the back, is at a different temperature from another part, such as the front. The result is a slight distortion in the shape of the mirror which can degrade the image it produces. In normal use some heating or cooling of a telescope mirror between day and night is almost inevitable, despite efforts to minimize it, and temperature differences as small as 0.2°C can cause trouble.

One way to overcome this problem would be to fabricate the mirror from fused silica, a form of ultra-pure glass made by melting the mineral quartz at around 2,000°C. Its advantage is that it is 16 times less sensitive to changes in temperature than normal glass. But attempts to manufacture a silica mirror for the 200-inch telescope at Mount Palomar in the early 1930s had been abandoned because of technical difficulties and escalating cost.

For Mount Palomar, and for the INT, there was another option: borosilicate glass. This, as its name implies, contains more of the element boron than normal glass. Its thermal expansion is only one third that of normal glass. A version with the trade name Pyrex had been introduced by the Corning Glass Works in New York State in 1915 and become enormously popular for ovenproof kitchenware. By the 1930s a type of Pyrex was also being tried – with some difficulty – for telescope mirrors including, in 1934-5, the one for Palomar.

By 1947 the INT Board of Management had decided they would also use Pyrex for the 100-inch disc (known as a blank) which, when shaped and coated, would become the telescope's primary mirror. To do this, Pyrex would have to be prepared by mixing the ingredients in a furnace, and then ladled into a mould to cast the disc, which would then have to be slowly cooled (annealed) over a period of several months. The task was made harder by the fact that when Pyrex melts, at a temperature over 1,500°C, it produces an extremely viscous liquid which flows like cold treacle. Pouring this into a mould is not easy, and the resulting blanks usually contained folds, streaks (known as striae), and even bubbles. (As mentioned earlier, such defects will not impair the performance of the finished mirror provided they do not affect the reflecting surface.) Because the relevant expertise was not yet available on this side of the Atlantic, Messrs Pilkington Brothers of St Helens, Lancashire, were commissioned to start investigating the problems of casting in Pyrex. Experimental casting of a number of small discs was carried out, but before Pilkingtons could progress to the full-size one, scheduled for March 1949, the order was cancelled. By what appeared to be a stroke of good fortune the Board had been offered a ready-made Pyrex blank as an outright gift.

The story of this disc, which eventually became the primary mirror of the INT at Herstmonceux, begins with an initiative by the American astronomer Heber D. Curtis in the 1930s. Curtis had come to prominence in 1920 as an advocate of the island universe theory – subsequently proved correct – which held that our galaxy is one of many. By the 1930s he was Director of the observatories of the University of Michigan, where he designed a large reflector for the observatory at Ann Arbor, near Detroit. This was to be an 86-inch instrument, and its mirror blank was to be a Pyrex one from Corning.

The equipment used at Corning Glass Works at this time for producing large mirror blanks consisted of three separate ovens. The first, and hottest, was the *melting tank*, into which the raw ingredients of glass were poured at the top, and from which the molten glass eventually emerged at the bottom. For all forms of glass the main ingredient is sand (silicon dioxide) which for Pyrex amounts to some 80 per cent of the total. The boron compound (boric oxide) which gives Pyrex its special properties contributes most of the remainder. The melting tank had to be kept at a temperature of 1,525°C for several days to allow the ingredients to mix and form molten glass.

The moulds into which the molten glass would be poured were contained in the *casting oven,* which had a domed roof and doors to admit the ladles for pouring in the molten glass. Each mould was constructed in refractory (temperature-resistant) bricks, and resembled a straight-sided circular paddling-pool, whose diameter determined the diameter of the finished disc and whose depth determined its thickness. If, as was often the case, the finished mirror was required to have a hole at its centre, a straight-sided plug was fixed at the centre of the mould. To cast a mirror blank, molten glass was brought in ladles from the melting tank to the casting oven, a distance of only a few feet. As each ladle was emptied, its load of liquid glass spread out over the surface of the glass already in the mould. Each ladle had a long handle and was manoeuvred by a gang of men, the weight of the ladle being taken by an overhead monorail. Working for hours on end with molten material at a temperature above red-heat demanded stamina as well as skill and concentration.

The casting oven at Corning Glass Works, photographed during the pouring of the first 200-inch disc in 1934. The disc that would become the INT mirror was poured in this oven two years later.

When pouring was complete, the mould and its contents were moved to the *annealing kiln.* This was a drum-shaped oven, electrically-heated, whose temperature could be precisely controlled. Here the mirror blank would be slowly cooled at a steady rate over a period that ranged from a few days or weeks for small mirrors to many months for the largest ones. If the temperature were lowered too rapidly, the outer layers of the mirror would begin to solidify while the interior was still soft. Then as the inside cooled further it would contract, setting up stresses inside the blank that would tend to distort its shape and might even cause it to crack. Annealing was a crucial stage in the production of a good mirror, ensuring that it cooled so slowly that all parts of it were effectively at the same temperature all the time. Only when annealing was complete was it possible to inspect the mirror closely and assess its quality.

The 86-inch Pyrex disc for Curtis' planned Michigan telescope was cast on 3rd April 1934. For months it was slowly cooled in its annealing kiln, but when it finally emerged for inspection it was found to be faulty. There were too many defects in the glass to allow it to be made into a successful mirror. The glassworks would have to supply a replacement, but before they could do so, Curtis had revised his plans, increasing the size of mirror he required to 98 inches.

In the meantime, Corning had been occupied with their largest project: production of the 200-inch disc for Mount Palomar Observatory. A first attempt at casting this had taken place in March 1934. The disc was twice the size of any made before, and its casting caught the public imagination and became a focus for worldwide media attention. But this disc too was a failure. Part of the mould had broken loose as the glass was ladled in, so the disc had to be discarded (and can now be seen in the Corning Museum of Glass in New York State). A second pouring, conducted without the media spotlight, proved successful, and the 200-inch blank finally left the glassworks in March 1936, at the end of the long annealing process. It was transported across the continent by rail to the laboratory in California where grinding and polishing of the mirror was to be carried out.

With the 200-inch disc out of the way, preparations for casting the 98-inch disc for Michigan University – and eventually for Herstmonceux – could begin at Corning Glass Works. On 10th June 1936 the mixing oven was fired up and the process of preparing some tens of tons of molten Pyrex begun. A mould was made for the 98-inch and installed inside the same large casting oven as had been used for the 200-inch Palomar disc. Alongside it in the same oven were moulds for a 76-inch disc for another customer, and four smaller discs. Casting of all six discs took place between 13th and 15th July.

The 98-inch blank was transferred into the annealing kiln that had previously housed the 200-inch Palomar disc, and the process of slow controlled cooling began. Annealing would take nine months, and was an anxious time for the glassworks staff and particularly for the special projects officer, George McCauley. Several of Corning's Pyrex discs had proved to be duds, and McCauley was not confident this one would be any better. Anxiety was compounded when the transformer supplying the annealing kiln heaters failed and the disc, then at 355°C, began to cool rapidly. But power was restored after two and a half hours, and the five degree drop in temperature was not thought to be enough to cause serious stress problems.

When the 98-inch blank finally emerged from the annealing kiln in April 1937, McCauley's worst fears seemed justified. Writing in his memoirs in the 1960s[1], he recalled that the underside of the disc was covered in 'a veritable sea of checks' (short cracks within the glass), about an inch deep and covering the entire lower surface. Greatly dismayed, McCauley expected the blank to be declared a failure, but the final decision rested with the man who had commissioned it, Heber Curtis. He was less pessimistic, and thought the problem might be overcome by removing the bottom layer of glass. After Corning's had sandblasted away the lower surface, Curtis inspected the disc again and decided that it would after all be usable, particularly since even more material would be cut away in the next stage of the mirror's preparation. Other defects in the blank, such as large streaks and numerous small bubbles (easily visible to the naked eye inside the disc today), were not thought to be an insuperable problem. Flawed but usable, the 98-inch blank was crated and shipped to Michigan in November 1937.

And there it remained. Curtis' ambition to build a large telescope for the Ann Arbor Observatory came to nothing. By the time he had completed the plans, economic depression meant that funds for the observatory were no longer available. Curtis himself was in his sixties and would die in 1942. The crated 98-inch blank, 18 inches thick and weighing 4.7 tons, would remain untouched for more than ten years. Its manufacture had cost $15,000, paid for by the McGregor Fund, a charity active in the Detroit area of Michigan, giving grants 'to relieve the misfortunes and promote the well-being of mankind'[2].

The first inkling that this 98-inch blank might be available for the INT came in a letter which reached the Astronomer Royal in late May or early June 1948. It was sent from America by Dr Albert Uttley, an electronics expert from the Telecommunications Research Establishment at Malvern, who was on a fact-finding tour of observatories in the United States. Uttley was leader of a team which was building one of the first computers developed in Britain, and would go on to work in the field of artificial intelligence. In 1948 he was also an adviser to the INT Board of Management, with expertise on control systems and automatic guiding of telescopes, and his visit to the US was to study current practice there. While visiting the University of Michigan Observatory, where his host was the director, Dr Leo Goldberg,

Uttley learned of the existence of the spare 98-inch blank and was told it was available for purchase. The suggested price was $25,000, including a 27-inch secondary blank, and an 11-inch Pyrex plug to fit the centre hole of the 98-inch disc. Presumably for political reasons this offer was not open to the Russians, who were also seeking a large disc. Uttley was taken to see the 98-inch blank. He dusted off a section of it and shone a torch inside. Despite seeing the numerous small bubbles in the glass he was able to report that 'everyone considers the disc to be a very good one'[3]. Earlier misgivings about the quality of the blank seem to have been forgotten in the intervening years.

Three weeks later there was even better news. Goldberg wrote to Uttley that he had spoken to the president of the McGregor Fund, owners of the 98-inch blank, and was now 'reasonably certain that the McGregor Fund would want to make an outright gift of the mirror blanks'[4]. This offer, if formally made, would place the Astronomer Royal, Spencer Jones, in something of a dilemma. Accepting it would mean that the INT would no longer be an all-British venture, and that the understanding that Pilkington Brothers would cast the disc in this country would have to be broken. The reduction in diameter from 100-inch to 98-inch would reduce the telescope's light-gathering power by four per cent, but this was something the astronomers could live with. On the plus side, acceptance of the Michigan disc would save a certain amount of money, perhaps £8,000 to £10,000, and, more important, it would save time. Completion of the telescope would come two years sooner if the Michigan disc were used, it was said – a claim that would not be borne out by events, since other factors would delay the completion of the telescope by much more than two years. Acquisition of the disc would bring further benefit by adding impetus to the INT project, which would be seen to be actually under way if such a large component, the very heart of the telescope, could be seen and touched. In the end, with the support of Alan Barlow at the Treasury, it was decided to accept the offer.

To formalise the deal, a carefully worded letter was sent to the Chairman of the McGregor Trustees, Judge Henry S. Hulbert, in September 1948. In it Spencer Jones wrote that he would be 'much interested to learn under what terms it would be possible to obtain the disk', and went on to explain that it would be very difficult to pay for it 'because of a shortage of dollars ... arising from the difficult economic position to which we have been reduced by the heavy cost of the recent war ...'[5]. The reply was five months in coming (Judge Hulbert had had a stroke), and reached Spencer Jones while he was travelling on business in the United States: the McGregor Trustees had agreed, unanimously, to make an outright gift of the disc, plus the two smaller items, to the Royal Greenwich Observatory.

The convoy carrying the 98-inch disc leaves Ann Arbor at the start of its journey to Britain in 1949. The disc is in the wooden crate carried on a trailer, visible left of centre.

Spencer Jones formally accepted the gift, and the 98-inch blank and its two companion pieces were sent by train to New York in late July 1949 and loaded aboard the *S.S. Maidan* for the Atlantic crossing. The three crates were unloaded at London's Surrey Docks on 8th August, only slightly delayed by a strike of dockers, and transported by road to Greenwich for safe storage. News of the gift, and of the arrival in Britain of the largest single piece of glass outside North America, was widely reported in the newspapers. It was good publicity for the Isaac Newton Telescope project. But obtaining the blank was only the first stage in making the telescope's primary. Turning it into a usable mirror would be a difficult and worrying process which would take several years.

Sir Howard Grubb ran the famous telescope-making company for 57 years. The firm went on to build the INT and many other important telescopes.

The firm entrusted with this was the grandly-named Sir Howard Grubb, Parsons and Company, usually referred to simply as 'Grubb Parsons'. Its founder, Thomas Grubb, had been the chief engineer of the Bank of Ireland, and began building telescopes and other scientific instruments as a sideline in the early nineteenth century. Among those to whom he supplied components was William Parsons, third earl of Rosse, builder of the Leviathan telescope mentioned earlier. Thomas Grubb's son Howard followed him into the telescope-making business, and took it over in 1875. As Sir Howard Grubb he built the Dublin-based firm into the best-established astronomical instrument maker in the world, supplying, amongst many others, three telescopes which are now at Herstmonceux, in Domes A, D, and E of the Equatorial Group. By 1925, in the aftermath of the First World War, the firm was in trouble and was bought out by Sir Charles Parsons, son of the third earl of Rosse and a keen astronomer himself in addition to being the inventor of the steam turbine.

The company re-established itself as Sir Howard Grubb, Parsons and Company, in premises adjacent to the parent company's turbine works in Newcastle-upon-Tyne. The manufacturing tradition of the turbine works was useful in telescope manufacturing also, since both products involve heavy engineering to extremely high precision.

Telescopes built by the Grubb Parsons company in the 1920s and 30s included the two 36-inch reflectors, one for Edinburgh and the other for Greenwich (now in Dome B at Herstmonceux) which were the largest in Britain at that time. The firm went on to supply another 36-inch reflector to Cambridge University Observatory in the mid-1950s. The largest telescopes built by Grubb Parsons prior to working on the INT were 74-inch reflectors supplied to observatories in Toronto and Pretoria and elsewhere. (The primary mirror for the second of these had been ordered from the Corning Glass Works in 1934, spent part of the Second World War buried in a field for safekeeping, and was finally delivered in 1948.)

Grubb Parsons were involved with the development of the INT from 1950 onwards. From then until the inauguration of the telescope in the following decade the General Manager and Chief Engineer was George M. Sisson. Few in the world knew as much as he did about telescope-building, and his would be the responsibility for both the detailed design and the ultimate delivery of the telescope. One of his innovations in telescope design is known as 'Sisson's fiddle' both from its shape and its *ad hoc* nature. Sisson is an unsung hero of the whole INT project, a voice of sanity throughout the many years of frustration and exasperation that lay ahead as the astronomers vacillated and prevaricated. (Asked on one occasion for his views on astronomers, Sisson replied that they were all right one at a time, but two or more could never agree.)

The INT would turn out to be the last telescope to be designed as well as built by Grubb Parsons; later instruments would be constructed to designs supplied by others. These would include the 1.2-metre (48-inch) UK Schmidt telescope at Siding Spring in New South Wales, the 3.9-metre (153-inch) Anglo-Australian Telescope, also at Siding Spring, and the 3.8-metre (150-inch) UK Infrared Telescope in Hawaii. The company would remain in business until the mid-1980s, its final product being also the largest, the 4.2-metre (165-inch) William Herschel reflector on La Palma in the Canary Islands.

The two main processes for making a mirror from a blank – well known to generations of amateur mirror-makers – are *grinding* and *polishing*. Grinding removes glass to give the front surface of the blank the required curved shape, usually concave. As the name implies, it leaves the surface with the texture of ground glass. Polishing converts this to a smooth shiny surface, ready to receive the reflective coating. A further process, *figuring*, akin to polishing, ensures the final shape of the mirror complies exactly with the telescope-designer's requirements.

To grind a blank by hand, starting from flat, a tool is needed. This is a flat glass disc similar to the blank itself, and is placed face up on a table. The blank is placed, face down, on top of the tool, with a layer of abrasive between them. This is a slurry containing grains of a material such as silicon carbide (Carborundum). These grains are so hard that when the tool is pushed back and forward they gouge small chips out of the surfaces of the blank and the tool, gradually grinding them down. Care must be taken to ensure that the tool is rotated frequently, and the direction and length of the grinding strokes varied. If this is done correctly, the blank gradually acquires a concave spherical surface, while the tool becomes convex, the two fitting together perfectly. The glass chips are washed away with the abrasive.

The Isaac Newton disc at Grubb Parsons' works. One of the polishing tools stands in the background.

For a large mirror, grinding by machine is essential. This time the blank is below, face up, and the tool on top. Movement of the blank and tool is motor-driven, in a way that gives the necessary randomness. As before there is a layer of abrasive between the two. Careful control of the pressure of the tool, and of its motion, ensures that the blank gradually assumes a concave spherical shape. This technique was used for the Isaac Newton mirror, but not before another shaping method, diamond milling, had been applied.

Milling is a process by which metal or other material is shaped by gradually cutting away unwanted material using a rotating tool – similar to a dentist enlarging a tooth cavity with a drill. For milling glass the tool has tiny diamonds embedded in it, and it is these diamonds that nibble away at the glass.

Once the mirror has been ground or milled to shape, polishing can begin. This is similar to grinding, except that the tool is given a softer surface, such as pitch, and the polishing agent between the tool and the mirror is a powder, such as an iron oxide, or more recently cerium oxide, whose grains are very much finer than those used in grinding. Polishing must be done under ultra-clean conditions, since the presence of even a single grain of grit could cause a scratch that would set the process back by several weeks.

The INT blank arrived at the Grubb Parsons works in Newcastle in April 1950. At this stage, according to Sisson, looking through it was like looking through marmalade. The first task was to true up the disc by milling away material from both faces and then polishing them to give a flat shiny finish. This process reduced the thickness of the disc from about 18 inches to about 16 inches. It also made it possible to study its interior in detail. The bubbles and striae already mentioned were now clearly visible, as was a crescent-shaped silvery streak which became known, for obvious reasons, as the diamond tiara. The next decision was whether the upper or lower surface should be hollowed out to the concave shape required for the mirror, a process which would involve laboriously removing a further two inches depth of glass (near the centre) and would bring to the surface a number of the flaws already existing in the disc. It was eventually decided that the surface that had been at the bottom when the disc was cast should be hollowed out to become the front surface of the finished mirror, and the slow process of shaping it began. This was done at first by diamond milling, but before work had progressed very far an alarming development occurred in the form of a new system of cracks which developed within the glass. Work was suspended at once but the crack system continued to spread for another two weeks. The Cambridge astronomer Edward Lintott was despatched to Newcastle to report on the crack system, which he described as having 'the glittering appearance of a crystallised ichthyosaurus preserved in aspic'[6]. It was decided to leave the disc for at least a year to settle down.

When work eventually restarted, the traditional slow method of grinding with carborundum was adopted as this was thought to put less strain on the surface being worked than diamond milling. (The diamond tiara and ichthyosaurus can still be seen today. With the disc in its current display position at the Observatory Science Centre at Herstmonceux, the tiara is at about 11 o'clock, three-quarters of the way out from the centre, and the ichthyosaurus at 4 o'clock, half-way out from the centre.)

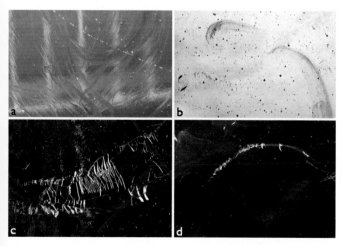

Inside the 98-inch disc: a – 'like looking through marmalade'; b – bubbles and striae; c – the 'crystallised ichthyosaurus'; d – the 'diamond tiara'. Despite the disc's many internal defects, Grubb Parsons were able to give a fine optical finish to the only part that mattered, the front surface.

Ex-Grubb Parsons machines were later transferred to University College, London. Here a metal mirror, newly-made for the restored 'Leviathan of Parsonstown', can be seen on the 2.5-metre polishing machine.

Here the polishing tool rests on top of the mirror on its rotating base. The tool is moved by two rigid motor-driven arms aligned at right angles.

Moving the huge mirror from machine to machine within the Grubb Parsons works was a tricky operation. On one occasion an operator error sent the suspended mirror gliding inexorably towards a steel girder. Disaster was averted by a quick thinking employee, David Sinden, who placed his hand and shoulder in the way; the mirror escaped damage, but he vowed never to repeat the manoeuvre.

Years passed, but by 1955 the mirror had substantially completed its grinding and polishing stages. To fulfil its role in a telescope, a mirror's surface is required to have no errors (humps or dips) whose height or depth is more than a small fraction of the wavelength of light. Tests showed that the INT mirror met the agreed specification, which was that it should be true to within one tenth of a wavelength, or two millionths of an inch – equivalent to a hill less than one inch high on a featureless plain the size of England. But tests done with the mirror horizontal and supported on an air cushion, had given slightly different results from those with the mirror vertical. This was evidence that the mirror, despite its thickness, was 'floppy', the precise shape of its surface – its figure – depending on the way in which the disc was supported. It was clear that great care would be needed to ensure the mirror was correctly supported when mounted inside the telescope. The test results also emphasised how sensitive the shape of the mirror's surface was to changes in the surrounding temperature, despite being made of low-expansion Pyrex. This temperature sensitivity would prove a considerable handicap to astronomers using the finished telescope.

In addition to its primary mirror, the INT – still planned to be usable as a Schmidt camera – would require a second major optical component, the corrector plate. This would be a specially shaped sheet of glass, about an inch thick, mounted at the skyward end of the telescope. Light would pass through this plate on its way into the telescope, and it was therefore essential that it be made of the finest optical-quality glass. In 1954 a sheet of plate glass to form the corrector plate was ordered from Pilkington Brothers. This was eventually delivered, but because of a change of plan was never given its final shape and put to use in the telescope. The plate remained a curiosity at Herstmonceux for many years and was finally disposed of after being accidentally damaged.

The long haul 4

DESPITE THE NEAR COMPLETION of work on the primary mirror, progress on the INT was painfully slow in the early 1950s. Bringing the project to fruition was going to be a long haul. In particular two questions of mechanical design were still unresolved. The first concerned the construction of the telescope itself – the way in which the optical components were to be held in place. The second was the question of the telescope's mounting – the structure that supports it and allows it to point to all parts of the sky.

For a small telescope a metal tube is adequate to hold the optical components in place. But scaled up to the dimensions required for the INT, such a tube would become impossibly heavy and insufficiently rigid. Instead, the largest telescopes are constructed from a framework of rigid struts.

By choosing to build a dual-purpose telescope, the INT Board had set itself an extremely hard task. The chosen design meant that the telescope tube would need to be a long one – 50 feet overall. It would have to carry the heavy mirror at one end and the corrector plate at the other, but must not bend by more than five thousandths of an inch when moved from the vertical to the horizontal position, or the optical performance would suffer. To advise on how to achieve the necessary rigidity, the engineer Barnes Wallis was brought in. Best known today for his work on the dam-busting bouncing bombs that proved so effective in the Second World War, Wallis had also worked on the structural framework of aircraft and it was this experience that was relevant to the construction of the INT.

In 1949 Wallis produced a report which showed that the required lack of bending could not be achieved unless some form of compensation was used. This would be a mechanism which would counteract the unavoidable slight bending of the framework when the telescope's position changed by causing it to bend in the opposite direction by a precisely controlled amount. At first he suggested that this compensation could be achieved by a thermal method. The telescope's framework would consist of hollow tubes which could be made to lengthen or shorten slightly by pumping a warm or cool liquid through them. Later a hydraulic method of compensation was considered, in which the tubes of the framework would be filled with oil under pressure. By increasing this pressure, a tube could be made to lengthen slightly, so counteracting any unwanted bending of the framework. In this way the framework could be artificially stiffened – made to appear more rigid than the uncompensated framework would be.

To test the feasibility of this method of artificial stiffening, a test rig was commissioned from engineers at Cambridge University. Preliminary results showed that the apparent stiffness of a steel tube could be increased by a factor of eight by this means, but no decision was taken to pursue this avenue further.

The second aspect of the telescope's design, how it was to be mounted, was more easily resolved. The mounting is a very important part of any telescope. It must be robust enough to hold the telescope tube without the slightest vibration or play and it must allow the telescope to turn smoothly to point to as much of the sky as possible. It must also incorporate a drive mechanism that will compensate for the Earth's rotation by turning the telescope to track the apparent movement of the stars across the sky in the course of the night.

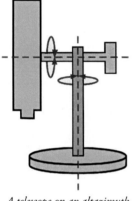

A telescope on an altazimuth mount.

There are two main types of telescope mount. In the *altazimuth* version the telescope stands on a horizontal base. To view all parts of the sky it can swing up and down about a horizontal axis, and from side to side about a vertical one. The *equatorial* mount is similar, except that the whole structure is tilted over at such an angle that its base is parallel to the Earth's equator. What was originally the vertical axis is now called the polar axis, and is parallel to the Earth's axis of rotation. This greatly simplifies the tracking process: to follow the movement of a star across the sky during the night the telescope must simply be rotated about the polar axis at a steady speed equal and opposite to that of the Earth's rotation.

At the time the INT was planned all large telescopes were equatorially mounted and it was a foregone conclusion that the INT would be too. Only in the 1970s, with the advent of computer control for the tracking mechanism, did it become feasible to build large altazimuth instruments, and all large new telescopes are now of this type. In 1954 the INT's Mechanical Design Committee, having considered various types of equatorial mounting, finally settled on the fork type, in which the telescope tube is held between the jaws of a massively strong fork, and can turn about an

A telescope on an equatorial mount.

axis running through these jaws. As originally planned, the handle of the fork would be an 'inverted truncated cone', similar in shape to an upside-down flowerpot, but this was later changed. As finally constructed, the INT had – and has – the two prongs of the fork mounted on a turntable, known as the polar disc, which is tilted at an angle that makes it parallel with the Earth's equator. The tracking system consists simply of a motor which rotates this disc at a steady speed that exactly compensates for the Earth's own rate of rotation. The telescope must be movable with extreme precision since the required pointing accuracy for the INT, whose moving parts would weigh 87 tons, would be better than one second of arc. This is 1/3600 of a degree of angle, or about 1/2000 of the diameter of the full moon.

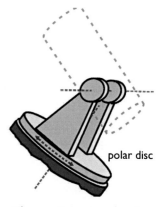

polar disc

The mounting system adopted for the INT. The polar disc can rotate and is tilted at an angle that makes it parallel to the Earth's equator.

For three years the telescope's Board of Management did not hold a single meeting. By February 1954 its members were becoming concerned at the lack of progress, which was partly explained by the need fully to investigate the stiffening system proposed by Barnes Wallis before any further decision could be taken. Further concern was expressed at the another meeting in November, and in December the Board finally decided to act – by appointing another committee. Called the Executive Committee, this would be different from all the others. With just three members it could meet at short notice and would be geared towards swift and decisive action. Its chairman was to be Roderick Redman, Professor of Astrophysics at Cambridge and a man with much practical experience of using telescopes. The other members were Harry Plaskett, still Professor of Astrophysics at Oxford, and Robert Atkinson, who was Spencer Jones' right-hand man at the Royal Observatory. George Sisson, from Grubb Parsons, was invited to attend the meetings.

The Executive Committee met six times in its first three months of existence. From the start, doubts resurfaced about the wisdom of staying with the proposal for a dual-purpose, or 'duplex' telescope. The Committee was divided on the issue, with two members favouring the duplex proposal and one, Redman, very uneasy about it and preferring a simpler design. The matter was referred back to the Board of Management which discussed it at length at its meeting in July 1955. This was the last meeting presided over by Harold Spencer Jones, who had reached retirement age and would soon cease to be Astronomer Royal. Nine years had elapsed since the Isaac Newton Telescope was first mooted. The question of why progress was so slow under his guidance is one we will return to later (page 91). One suggestion is that, as Director of the Royal Observatory, Spencer Jones did not wish to be seen to be taking over the new telescope, which was not to be part of the observatory. His successor would have no such scruples.

At the July 1955 Board meeting, Spencer Jones spoke out firmly for the 'no turning back' option, with the result that the members 'appeared on balance to favour adhering to the principle of a duplex telescope'. There was one important proviso, however. The decision would not be confirmed as final unless the new Astronomer Royal concurred with it. The question of the proposed siting of the telescope was also reviewed at this meeting, and here the Board was unanimous. The telescope was for the benefit of British astronomy, it commemorated a British scientist, and was for the use of all observatories in the United Kingdom. The Board unanimously affirmed that the telescope should be erected in Britain as planned, and confirmed that a site had been earmarked at Herstmonceux.[1]

Harold Spencer Jones retired at the end of 1955 and was subsequently rewarded with a K.B.E., a second knighthood to add to his existing one. His successor as Astronomer Royal was Richard van der Riet Woolley. Though British by birth, Woolley had strong connections with South Africa, and spent some of his childhood and part of his working life there. He had also worked at the Mount Wilson observatory in California, and in the 1930s had been Chief Assistant at Greenwich. As Astronomer Royal he would oversee the final stages of the observatory's move to Herstmonceux. Under his leadership the observatory would flourish, its contribution to astronomical research would increase, and its fame and prestige would be enhanced. Under Woolley's 'brusque good humour and towering personality', these would be 'halcyon days indeed' when, in the words of one who was there at the time, 'it was a pleasure and a privilege to work at Herstmonceux'[2].

Richard Woolley (1906-86), Astronomer Royal from 1956 to 1971.

Woolley was also the man who would finally bring the Isaac Newton Telescope to completion. Even before he arrived at the RGO, he had expressed strong views about the proposed new telescope, suggesting that it should not be built in Britain at all, but somewhere in the southern hemisphere. At a time when most of the world's more powerful telescopes were sited at observatories in the northern hemisphere, leaving southern skies relatively unexplored, there was some logic in this suggestion. But politics outweighed logic, and the Board of Management reaffirmed the original decision to build the INT at Herstmonceux. Woolley himself would go on to play a leading role in the setting up of what was, when it opened, the southern hemisphere's largest telescope. This was the 150-inch Anglo-Australian telescope which entered service in 1974 after a gestation period almost as long as that of the INT.

Nineteen fifty-six would be a crucial year for the INT Project. When the Board of Management met on 5th March, Woolley was in the chair for the first time (and Spencer Jones was a member). Woolley had already discussed the project at an informal gathering of astronomers attending an international meeting in Dublin, and his mind was made up. He told the Board that after much consideration and discussion he had reached a firm conclusion that he could not take responsibility for a duplex instrument. A conventional reflector would be far better. A vote was taken, and the Board, which eight months earlier had agreed 'on balance' to proceed with the duplex plan, now voted unanimously to abandon it.[3] In the light of Woolley's remarks, they had no choice. The Isaac Newton Telescope would be a reflector of the tried and tested Cassegrain type.

With this decision the principal barrier to progress, the exacting mechanical requirement, was removed. The INT project could now move forward using, for the most part, existing technology. The estimated time to completion would be shortened from six or seven years to five or six, and there would be cost savings, not least because the simpler design produced a much shorter telescope – 27 feet long instead of 50 – which would fit into a smaller dome. The 98-inch mirror would require refiguring to change its shape from spherical to paraboloid – a small change, though it would take about a year to complete. No major reshaping of the mirror would be possible because of a number of surface cracks. According to Sisson, these would be 'annoying but not detrimental'.

One group of astronomers would lose out by the decision to abandon the dual-purpose design. They were the people whose researches would have made use of the INT in its wide-angle (Schmidt camera) mode, which would not now be available. Some consolation would eventually come with the opening in 1973 of the 48-inch UK Schmidt telescope in Australia.

At the March 1956 meeting of the Board of Management, Woolley instituted one further change. The Executive Committee would be reformed, with full operational powers and increased authority. Woolley himself would become its chairman. By the end of the meeting the Isaac Newton project not only had a clearer view of its destination, but also a more powerful driving force to get it there.

Woolley's arrival breathed new life into the INT project. At a stroke he had overcome the major obstacle to progress. Yet the road to completion would still be a rocky one, and eleven more years would elapse before the telescope was open for business.

The first task for the revitalised Executive Committee was to work out the details of the telescope's design and specifications and pass these to the Admiralty, which was still responsible for the Royal Observatory and would let the contracts for the construction of the telescope and dome. But before this could be done a sudden clampdown on government spending brought the project to an abrupt halt, early in 1958. The country's finances were in a precarious state and inflation was rising. As part of a general cost-cutting exercise spending on the INT project was frozen *sine die*. Even the preliminary design work being done at Grubb Parsons had to stop. A protest was raised in the House of Commons, but to no avail. Woolley must have wondered whether funding for a 100-inch telescope would ever be forthcoming again, and as a possible fallback he invited Grubb Parsons to quote for a smaller, 74-inch reflector. The firm had supplied telescopes of this size before, so its production would be a much more straightforward matter.

The spending freeze turned out to be temporary, however, and funding for the INT was reinstated early in the following year. As before, the money would come from the government by two routes: half of it directly from the Treasury and the other half via the Admiralty. This arrangement added to the administrative workload, since approval for all expenditure had to be sought from two separate departments. Nevertheless by December 1959 all the pieces of the jigsaw were in place, and the order for the INT was finally placed. Not surprisingly the telescope was to be constructed by Sir Howard Grubb, Parsons and Company. The parts would be fabricated at the firm's Newcastle works and the telescope assembled and tested there before being dismantled for shipping to Herstmonceux. The firm's tender to the Director of Navy Contracts was for the supply of one 98-inch reflecting telescope, complete and delivered but not erected, for the sum of £321,000. The delivery time was quoted as six years from the placing of the order.

Even while the telescope was beginning to take shape at Grubb Parsons' works there were last minute changes to its optical design. In 1962 Woolley acquiesced to a proposal that the two main mirrors – the primary and the secondary – should be given a shape very slightly different from what had earlier been decided. This arrangement, approximating to what is technically known as the Ritchey-Chrétien configuration, would increase the area of sky that could be successfully recorded on a single photographic plate. There would be a down side, however, with a loss of sharpness when the telescope was used in its simplest mode, and in 1964 Woolley reversed his decision, reverting to the conventional paraboloidal design. Since the 98-inch mirror had not yet undergone its final figuring, these changes of plan caused no extra delay or expense.

By 1964, visitors to the Newcastle works could see the INT standing in the main assembly shop. Its slewing motion about two axes could be demonstrated, even though it did not, as yet, carry any optical components. By June 1966 the telescope was virtually complete. Testing was almost finished, prior to the telescope's disassembly for the journey south.

In the meantime at Herstmonceux, the building to house the telescope was slowly taking shape. Like so much else about the INT project, progress had been held back by administrative complexity and disagreement about design. Responsibility for the construction of the lower part of the building lay initially with the Navy Works Department, while responsibility for the dome on top was with Grubb Parsons. The two parties were said to be continually arguing and a three-man Technical Sub-Committee was set up to sort out points of detail. In 1964 the Navy handed over to the Ministry of Public Building and Works (MPBW). Meetings between the Sub-Committee and the MPBW were described as stormy, with the latter being blamed for a succession of delays. Further upheaval came the following year, when responsibility for the whole INT project, and for the Royal Greenwich Observatory, passed to the newly-formed Science Research Council.

A site for the INT had been earmarked near the southeast corner of the Herstmonceux Castle estate, some 300 yards from the Equatorial Group – the cluster of six domes that was home to the observatory's existing research telescopes. It had also been decided that the telescope's dome would not sit at ground level, but at the top of a 48-foot tall cylindrical tower, referred to as the drum. By this means the telescope would be protected from the worst effects of being too near the ground, namely heating by day and mists by night.

A further precaution would be the planting of trees in the vicinity of the telescope. The site for the INT was originally on open ground, but under Woolley's direction thousands of trees

An aerial view of part of the Herstmonceux Castle estate shows the positions of the former RGO headquarters in the Castle, the Equatorial Group of telescopes (now the Observatory Science Centre) and the INT dome.

were planted on the observatory estate, many of them close to the INT, so that today the dome is surrounded by dense woodland. Tree cover reduces the heating of the ground on sunny days, thereby reducing the turbulence caused by rising warm air.

With an overall height approaching that of a ten-storey building, the INT would become a prominent feature of the Sussex landscape, and was likely to remain so throughout the telescope's planned working life of fifty years. From the south, where the land drops away sharply to the Pevensey Levels, the dome would dominate the skyline for miles around and even be visible to shipping in the English Channel. Naturally, for such a conspicuous feature, there was concern about what it would look like, and a dispute over its appearance developed between the astronomers and the observatory's consultant architect, Brian O'Rorke.

O'Rorke was a New Zealander who had come to prominence as an interior designer for ocean liners. In the early 1950s he was brought in to oversee the observatory's development at Herstmonceux, after the appearance of the first new building erected there had provoked a public outcry. Concern about the effect a major scientific institution would have on the Sussex landscape had even reached the national press, with one critic describing the observatory buildings as 'monstrous bulbous excrescences'.[4]

The architect stipulated a copper-clad dome for the INT, to match those of the nearby Equatorial Group, shown here, but he was overruled by the astronomers.

O'Rorke's main contribution had been as architect for the building to house the Equatorial Group of telescopes. His design for this was generally regarded as a success in architectural terms (and the building is now a Grade 2* listed monument), though it was unpopular with the astronomers who had to work there. Landscaping features such as raised walkways, a ha-ha and a large lily pond were unnecessary hazards for people moving around in total darkness, but a more serious drawback came from O'Rorke's choice of cladding material for the six domes. One function of a telescope dome is to keep the instrument inside as cool as possible during the day, so that it will not take too long to come into equilibrium when the dome is opened at night. For this reason modern practice is for astronomical domes to have a white or silver finish. For the Equatorial Group, however, O'Rorke wanted domes of a blue-green colour which would fade into the horizon when seen from a distance. To achieve this he stipulated cladding in copper sheet, which though dark when new has now weathered, as intended, to greenish-blue. But in use the domes and their contents warmed up more than was desirable, particularly on sunny days, and valuable observing time was lost waiting for them to cool down in the evening.

In 1961 the Board of Management specified copper cladding for the drum and dome of the INT. This was to be spray-painted with titanium dioxide, chosen both for its thermal properties and it durability. The whole building would be a gleaming white. O'Rorke, on the other hand, wanted a two-tone building, with the dome left as unpainted copper, so that it would eventually turn green to match the domes of the nearby Equatorial Group. But the Board overruled him, declaring it 'wrong that aesthetic decisions should outweigh scientific ones'[5]. In the end, however, they agreed that the building should be clad all over in aluminium rather than copper, and this is what was done. Unpainted aluminium was not ideal, however; in view of later problems with keeping the telescope cool, there seems little doubt that the titanium dioxide finish would have been better.

Construction work began at the end of 1964 with the laying of the foundation for the telescope, a massive piled raft of reinforced concrete. From this there rose the central pier, a three-sided hollow concrete pillar 48 feet tall, with platforms at the top to support the telescope and its mount and ancillary equipment. Work on the building itself – the cylindrical drum on which the dome would sit – began in mid-1965. To avoid the risk of vibration being transmitted to the telescope, the drum and dome were totally separate from the central pier. They had their own foundations and nowhere did they make rigid contact with the pier. Assembly of the 60-foot diameter hemispherical dome began at the start of 1966, and by the end of that year the components of the mount were being lifted into position by crane, followed by the telescope itself. At the end of August 1967, MPBW declared the project complete, apart from the installation of the main mirror, due the following month, the completion of tests, and various minor items. Transport of the crated mirror from Newcastle to Sussex appears to have passed without public notice, its arrival at Herstmonceux coinciding with a weekend cricket match on the Castle pitch. Play was briefly suspended while the driver came over to ask where to deliver his load.

Inevitably, perhaps, for a project that seemed to be as much about politics as it was about astronomy, there was continued sniping from the sidelines even while the plans were coming to fruition. One such attack reached the higher echelons of the British government. In June 1960 Enoch Powell M.P., a former

By July 1965 the concrete structure to support the telescope was complete, and the surrounding drum was under construction.

Treasury minister in Harold Macmillan's government, received a personal letter from a Dr Ray Lyttleton, with whom he had been at school.[6] Lyttleton was by then a distinguished astronomer, Reader in Theoretical Astronomy at Cambridge, with a reputation for questioning received wisdom, whether in matters of science policy or science itself. 'It has become clear,' he wrote, 'that Sussex is quite the wrong place for ... such an expensive piece of equipment' as the Isaac Newton Telescope. 'The Americans are having a good old chuckle at the idea of putting it in the Sussex marshes', he continued, adding that many in Britain were terrified of questioning the decision to site the telescope at Herstmonceux 'lest the powers that be get fed up and it ends with no telescope at all'. Powell forwarded Lyttleton's letter to his successor at the treasury, Sir Edward Boyle, in the hope that he might be able to prevent 'what smells like a nonsense'. Boyle thought there was 'a good deal of force' in what Lyttleton had to say, and passed the letter in turn to the Minister for Science, Viscount Hailsham.

Quintin Hogg, Viscount Hailsham, had a special reason to be interested. His family home was a few miles from Herstmonceux, and the town of Hailsham, from which he drew his title, is nearby. Forty years later he would be laid to rest in the graveyard of Herstmonceux parish church, just outside the gates of what was by then the former Royal Observatory. His immediate response, on seeing Lyttleton's letter, was that the INT should stay. He knew from his own experience that Herstmonceux had 'some of the clearest skies in the UK' and also believed, wrongly, that the newest of the existing telescopes there was 'something like 100 years old'. 'If it is worth keeping the Greenwich Observatory at all', he added (in a phrase that would have chilled the heart of the Astronomer Royal had he been aware of it), 'it is, I think, worth being a little more up to date'. He was particularly incensed by Lyttleton's reference to the 'Sussex marshes'.

Enoch Powell was not the only person to receive a letter from Ray Lyttleton at this time. Among other recipients was Bernard Lovell of Jodrell Bank, in his capacity as chairman of the Board of Visitors of the Royal Greenwich Observatory. This was a sort of Governing Body which had met annually since 1710 to watch over the operations of the Observatory. Lyttleton's letter asked the Board to give further consideration to the siting of the Isaac Newton Telescope. This it did at considerable length at its next meeting, while the Astronomer Royal, whose presence on these occasions was by invitation only, waited outside. Old history was retold, and old arguments revisited, particularly the assertion that the Sussex location would enable British astronomers to keep abreast of modern observational research, and encourage 'the progression of young astronomers'[7]. In the end, after reviewing the contrary arguments, the Board saw no justification for a change of policy.

Armed with this decision, and after receiving strongly worded advice in similar vein from the Royal Society and the Astronomer Royal, who had canvassed the opinion of colleagues outside the observatory, the Minister for Science sent a curt note back to Dr Lyttleton saying he was satisfied there were no grounds for him to overturn the original decision on where to put the INT. Only Sir Edward Boyle at the Treasury was 'not entirely happy' at the outcome, but felt it was now too late for the government 'to go into retreat on the Isaac Newton Telescope'. To a younger generation of astronomers the whole episode smacked of a stitch-up. Establishment figures had closed ranks and not opened their minds to the possibility that a decision which seemed right fifteen years earlier might now be wrong.

Criticism of a different nature came the following year, directed not just at the siting of the telescope but also at the quality of its primary mirror. In a debate on Science in the House of Commons, an M.P., Mr Arthur Skeffington, reported hearing that the 'valuable trial blank given to us by the United States has ... been ruined by a firm without adequate technical knowledge of this kind of work'. The story was totally without foundation, and Woolley was quick to deny it. But it must have gained some currency, since he later felt it necessary to point out, in a progress report to the Royal Astronomical Society, that the people who knew the mirror best, the staff of Grubb Parsons, had a good opinion of it. If there were really any need for a better blank, then

When new, the INT building stood out prominently on open ground (above). Forty years on, in this view from the Science Centre, only the dome is visible above the trees (below).

one could have been acquired at a cost that was modest compared to the total project budget. Large mirror blanks were much more easily obtainable than they had been fifteen years before.

Old wounds were reopened as late as 1964 in the course of a discussion about possible uses for the INT held at the annual Herstmonceux Conference of astronomers. In a closely reasoned contribution, a researcher from the Royal Observatory, Edinburgh, Peter Fellgett, argued with some force that a smaller telescope of the Schmidt type would have been a far more productive research tool than the Cassegrain design chosen for the INT. It was tragic, he said, that the state of knowledge at the time had allowed the wrong decision to be made[8]. Other delegates disagreed, however, and the matter blew over. By now attention was focussed on the final construction and testing of the telescope, and on the arrangements for its official opening.

As the date of this event approached, however, a last-minute hitch threatened to derail the proceedings. To improve insulation, the INT building had a cavity wall two feet thick, with aluminium on the outside and an inner skin of plywood insulated with expanded polystyrene and aluminium foil. Expanded polystyrene had recently been designated a serious fire-hazard, unacceptable in a building which had no external fire-escape and whose upper levels were beyond the reach of the local fire brigade. Luckily it was possible to commandeer a taller escape-ladder from some distance away, and when this was discreetly parked nearby the safety inspectors were satisfied and the opening ceremony could go ahead.

ISAAC NEWTON TELESCOPE
INAUGURATED BY
HER MAJESTY THE QUEEN
1ST DECEMBER 1967

The plaque unveiled by the Queen at the INT opening is now preserved at the La Palma observatory.

The Isaac Newton Telescope was officially inaugurated by Her Majesty the Queen on 1st December 1967 – twenty-one years and nine months after Harry Plaskett first floated the idea of a new national telescope in Britain. Among the privileged guests assembled in the dome at six o'clock that night were the Duke of Norfolk, the Minister for Education and Science, the Chairman of the Science Research Council, and from America, representatives of the McGregor Fund which had donated the mirror disc. The Astronomer Royal showed the Queen round the installation, presented her with a replica of Isaac Newton's original reflector, and invited her to unveil a plaque. When it was Her Majesty's turn to speak, she emphasised the role the new telescope would play in countering the brain drain – the haemorrhaging of highly-trained and talented people from Britain to North America which was a major concern at the time. 'Britain is a leader in radio astronomy', she continued, 'but lags behind in the building of optical telescopes. This monster', referring to the telescope, '... will redress the balance'[9].

The speeches over, Her Majesty went to the controls where she moved the telescope and made the dome rotate. Everyone then made their way over to the Castle, which was floodlit for the occasion, to join a larger gathering for an official reception in the ballroom.

Plans had been made for the Queen to return to the dome for a private session in which she would use the telescope to view the planet Saturn and perhaps some galaxies. The observer's chair had been specially adapted to suit someone of Her Majesty's stature, and tried out by an astronomer of similar height, who pronounced it very comfortable.[10] But in the event the sky was overcast and this part of the visit had to be abandoned.

The Queen and Astronomer Royal at the INT control desk, 1st December 1967.

The inauguration of the Isaac Newton Telescope in 1967 has been described as a 'joyful' occasion[11]. Twenty-one years of indecision and delay were at an end. Britain had an engineering masterpiece to be proud of, and British astronomers at last had a world-class instrument at their disposal. After two decades in which radio astronomy had led the field, British optical astronomy was due for a resurgence, and the INT would be part of it.

Press coverage of the event was extensive and largely favourable. One newspaper did mention the controversy over the site, but balanced it by pointing out that the Astronomer Royal saw one definite advantage in keeping the INT in Britain, namely its usefulness for training British astronomers in the techniques of working with large telescopes. Additional publicity came later from an advertising campaign launched by the North East Development Council, a body set up to promote the industrial potential of the area in which the telescope had been built. 'Heaven knows who made the stars,' it trumpeted, 'We just made the telescope'. 'Revolutionary technical advances' had been incorporated into the INT, including, it claimed, the 'unique air-floated mirror' which had been 'eagerly copied' by the Americans[12].

When all the bills were in, the total cost of the Isaac Newton Telescope came to a little under £1,000,000 – equivalent to about £15,000,000 at today's prices. Nearly half of this was for the telescope itself, and much of the rest for the building and dome. Officials at the Treasury, where the INT had been on the books for two decades, must have been greatly relieved to see the 'damned telescope' completed. The question of whether it represented money well spent was never far away, however, and would return with increasing insistence in the years ahead.

5 'The greatest telescope in Western Europe'

THE 'MONSTER' which the Queen inaugurated in Sussex in December 1967 was, according to Professor William McCrea, 'the greatest telescope in Western Europe'.[1] It was also the second largest telescope in the world outside North America, marginally outranked by a 102-inch reflector which had recently come into service at the Crimean Astrophysical Observatory in Russia.

At first sight the new telescope looked quite simple: the huge mirror peered out from the bottom of an open-lattice tube which could be swung round to point to whatever part of the sky was visible through the broad opening in the rotatable dome overhead. But in reality it was far from simple. The scientists who used the telescope would want to coax every last ounce of astronomical information from it. To satisfy them it had, despite its great size, to be an instrument of the utmost precision. Formidable engineering challenges had been faced – and hopefully overcome – in designing and constructing the telescope, its mount and the building to house it.[2]

It helped that the construction of the telescope had been in the hands of probably the most experienced and trusted firm in the business. Once the contract was finally let, Grubb Parsons delivered the telescope within budget, if allowance is made for inflation in the intervening years. That the construction period was seven years rather than the quoted six was not their fault. It is fitting that George Sisson, the Managing Director, should have been one of those selected to meet the Queen at the telescope's Inauguration.

One of the engineering challenges concerned, as already mentioned, the problem of rigidity. In use the telescope has to point in different directions, from the vertical to the near-

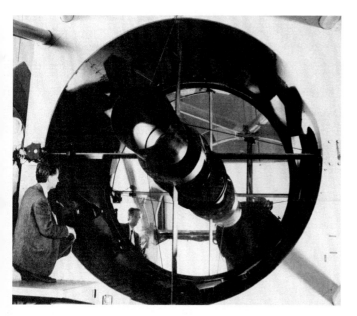

Inside the INT: an astronomer crouches inside the telescope and is seen reflected in the 98-inch mirror at the far end.

horizontal, and will inevitably change shape slightly due to the redistribution of weight as it moves. This is the problem which the abandoned Barnes Wallis scheme had been intended to overcome. In the finished INT a different solution was employed, known as 'symmetrical sag'. This had in fact been recommended for the INT by Dr Uttley following his fact-finding mission to the United States back in 1948, and it is not clear why it was not adopted sooner. The principle of symmetrical sag, also known as balanced flexure, had been devised by a Belgian engineer, Marc Serrurier, for the 200-inch Palomar telescope, and has been widely used in large telescopes built since that time.

The figure on the right shows how it was applied in the INT. As shown in the upper diagram the primary mirror is held in a rigid cell at the lower end of the telescope. This is supported by eight struts, forming four isosceles triangles, which spring from the sides of a massive square box placed at the centre of gravity of the telescope. The equipment mounted at the top end is held by a similar arrangement of longer struts springing from the same box. When the telescope is moved from the vertical to the horizontal position both ends will drop by a very small amount due to the stresses in the struts, as shown, greatly exaggerated, in the lower diagram. The ingenious feature of the Serrurier design is that by careful choice of the lengths and strengths of the two sets of struts, it can be arranged that the two ends of the telescope drop by exactly equal amounts, hence 'symmetrical sag'. The primary and secondary mirrors thus remain in perfect alignment, as indicated by the red dotted line, and the performance of the telescope is unaffected.

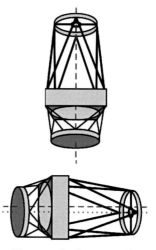

The principle of symmetrical sag, as applied in the INT.

Another significant engineering challenge arose from the way the primary mirror had to be supported. The cell that held it was a flat cylindrical box attached to the lower end of the telescope. The mirror must be held in position inside this cell extremely precisely, and must not distort under its own weight, or when the telescope swings from one position to another. For the INT the solution here involved supporting the telescope on a system of ring-shaped airbags to spread the weight, similar to large, rather flat, inflatable rubber rings. At the same time the back of the mirror was in contact with the tops of three small locating pads rising from the bottom of the cell. These pads could be raised or lowered by tiny amounts as a means of aligning the mirror precisely within the telescope. The pressure in the airbags was adjusted so that they carried almost all the weight of the mirror, effectively reducing the apparent weight of the disc from four tons to less than one pound, resting gently against the locating pads. The airbag pressures were also controlled to allow for the fact that the mirror is lighter near the centre, where it is thinner, than at the edges, and so needs less supporting pressure there. Whenever the angle of the telescope was altered, the pressures in the airbags had to be carefully adjusted, from a maximum when the telescope was pointing straight up and the bags had to carry almost the full weight of the mirror, to a minimum when the telescope was near-horizontal and the mirror was nearly on its side.

To prevent the mirror shifting sideways within the cell, an ingenious system of levers and counterweights exerted radial forces – push or pull – around its circumference to support it and reduce the stresses that would otherwise build up inside it due to its own weight when its angle of tilt altered. Three rigid pads fitted between the perimeter of the mirror and the inside wall of the cell made sure the mirror stayed precisely in position.

The mirror support system also incorporated an arrangement for keeping the mirror cool. A fibreglass plate with a large number of flexible studs rising from its upper surface was inserted between the airbags and the back of the disc, so that the mirror was supported by the studs. This meant that air could be circulated across the lower surface of the mirror. The upper side of the mirror cell was covered, when the telescope was not in use, by a shutter system. The intention was that cooled air would be circulated all round the mirror during the day, to maintain it at the expected night-time temperature.

The dome that housed the INT was a double-skinned insulated hemisphere 60 feet in diameter and weighing 120 tons, with electrically-driven shutters which opened to allow the telescope to see out. It was carried on rollers, and could be rotated under electric power. Further provision to reduce convection currents was incorporated into the design of the building, since turbulent currents in the air along a telescope's line of sight can impair its performance. When seen with the naked eye these currents cause the stars to twinkle. Astronomers call the same effect the 'seeing'. When the seeing is good there is little air turbulence and the image of a star in the telescope will be a tiny, steady point of light. But when the air is turbulent, for example after a hot day, the seeing is likely to be poor, and the image of a star will appear to flicker and dance about. Time-exposure photographs taken under these conditions will appear blurred. On the INT, large extractor fans were provided at ground level to draw down night air through the building and expel it at the bottom. It was hoped that this would counteract convection currents and 'clean up the seeing' around the top end of the telescope tube.

In the event, these precautions proved inadequate. A report compiled in 1974 detailed numerous factors that contributed to the telescope's temperature-sensitivity, including the fact that the intended refrigeration system had never been completed, and the fan to circulate air round the mirror proved ineffective and was removed. The only simple expedient was to keep the dome open at night as much as possible, even when the telescope was not in use, in order to keep it cool. But thermal effects were a continuing problem for INT users throughout its time at Herstmonceux.

Precision engineering on a grand scale was also involved in the construction of the telescope's fork mounting. The polar disc alone was 22 feet in diameter and three feet thick, and weighed approximately 40 tons – so large in fact that it could not be transported whole, but had to be dismantled into three sections for the journey from Newcastle to Herstmonceux. To ensure the disc could rotate freely when in situ, it was supported on a number of oil-pressure bearings so that the whole disc – and with it the telescope – was floating on films of oil a mere four thousandths of an inch in thickness. The polar disc itself, when mounted at the correct equatorial angle, was so finely balanced that the addition of a single coin near its edge was sufficient to set it in motion.

The design of the INT's mount, with the telescope held between two massive piers rising from a rotatable disc, was not in itself new. As long ago as the 1840s the engineer James Nasmyth had constructed a 20-inch reflector with several novel features. One of them was that it was mounted between two piers rising from a rotating platform. His instrument (now held by the Science Museum) had an altazimuth mount, which meant that the rotating platform was horizontal. Many later telescopes have used the same principle. What was different about the INT was that its rotating platform – the polar disc – was tilted to a position in which it lay precisely parallel to the plane of the Earth's equator. As mentioned earlier, this greatly simplifies the task of compensating for the Earth's rotation while making an observation.

James Nasmyth's 20-inch reflector, 1845. Its novel method of mounting, between supports rising from a rotatable disc, was also used for the INT.

The technique for coating the front surface of a mirror with aluminium was developed by the American physicist John Strong in the 1930s and used on a number of large telescopes including the Palomar 200-inch. Strong had discovered, unexpectedly, that a coating of aluminium – not normally a very shiny metal – produces a better reflecting surface than silver when deposited on a polished glass base in a layer about 1,000 atoms thick. To produce this layer, the uncoated disc, after careful cleaning, is lowered into a strong airtight metal chamber. Vacuum pumps then reduce the air pressure in the chamber to less than one 30-millionth of atmospheric pressure, producing a vacuum so high that individual atoms or molecules remaining in the tank can travel more than a metre without colliding with each other. A number of small coils of tungsten wire are mounted inside the tank, some distance from the front surface of the mirror, each with a piece of aluminium wire wrapped around it.

When the tungsten is heated to white heat by passing an electric current though it, the aluminium reaches a temperature at which it begins to evaporate. Atoms of aluminium boil off and travel towards the cold mirror surface where they condense. In this way the mirror's surface can be coated with an even layer of metal about one ten-thousandth of a millimetre in thickness, after which the air can be let back into the chamber. The advantage of using such a thin layer is that it takes the finish of the underlying surface, so that if the glass is finely-polished, the aluminium is also.

A further benefit of using aluminium is that the newly-created surface soon oxidises when the mirror is in the open air, producing a tough coating of transparent aluminium oxide which provides protection for the pure metal below without affecting its reflecting quality. Even so, with the mirror exposed to night air when the telescope is in use, its performance gradually deteriorates, and re-aluminising is required after a few months. In the design of the INT building, provision was made for regularly transferring the main mirror between the telescope on the upper floor and ground level, where the aluminising tank was situated. A crane in the roof of the dome was provided to raise and lower the mirror through a well which ran the whole height of the building. The whole process of removing the mirror from the telescope, lowering it to ground level, cleaning and recoating it, and reinstalling it could be carried out with the loss of only a single night's observing time.

The way the mirror was suspended from the crane involved a

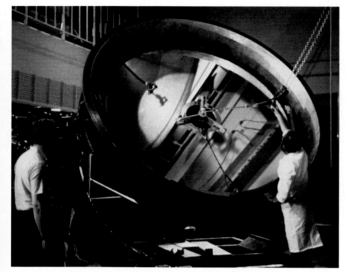

The INT's original aluminising plant was later moved to the Canary Islands. This photograph shows it in use there in the 1980s, with the new INT mirror about to be removed from the vacuum tank after re-surfacing.

flat ring attached to a plug that fitted from below into the hole in the centre of the mirror. Lifting it in this way put great strain on the centre portion of the mirror and on one occasion a scallop of glass split off at the edge of the hole. The damaged area can be seen on the mirror today, but fortunately only affected an area which in use was always covered by the shadow of parts of the telescope mount. This incident tended to confirm that despite its careful annealing there were still internal strains in the Pyrex disc.

Further complexity in the design of the INT arose from the fact that the telescope was to be used in three different modes, known respectively as prime focus, Cassegrain focus and coudé focus, and shown in the diagrams on the next page. Each had advantages and disadvantages for particular types of observation. In use the telescope would need to be switched between modes as often as once or twice a week, so the conversion process needed to be as straightforward as possible.

The prime focus configuration had the advantage of simplicity, and was used for direct photography of the night sky. In this configuration light falling onto the primary mirror was focussed onto a glass photographic plate mounted at the prime focus inside the tube near the top of the instrument, facing towards the mirror. A disadvantage was that the observer, in the initial years at least, had to ride inside a cramped metal cage bolted to the top end of the telescope. This had to be as small as possible to avoid obscuring much of the light entering the telescope.

The plates used at prime focus were quite small, eight centimeters square, so that each photograph covered an area of sky little broader than the width of the full moon. The image was only truly sharp near the centre. Further out, the inevitable distortions

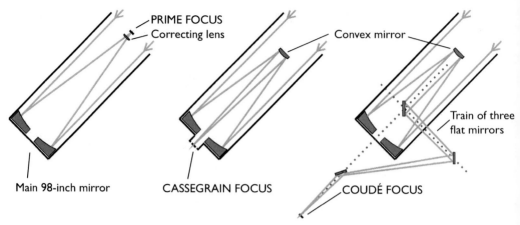

PRIME FOCUS
Correcting lens

Main 98-inch mirror

Convex mirror

CASSEGRAIN FOCUS

Train of three
flat mirrors

COUDÉ FOCUS

The INT was designed to operate in three different configurations, at prime focus, Cassegrain focus and coudé focus.

In the early days, the observer had to ride in a cage attached to the top of the telescope when using it in prime focus mode.

produced by a parabolic mirror, especially coma, became more and more noticeable. From mid-1969, however, the useful field of view could be greatly increased by mounting in front of the plate a complex correcting lens, known as a Wynne corrector after its designer, Professor Charles Wynne of Imperial College, London.

The second mode in which the INT could be, and most frequently was, used was the Cassegrain one. The photographic plateholder was removed from the top end of the telescope and a convex secondary mirror mounted in its place. This focussed the light back down the tube, through the central hole in the main mirror, to a point at the lower end of the telescope where a photographic plate or other equipment could be mounted. This had the advantage that bulky detecting equipment could be used without obstructing the light path through the telescope. It was also much more convenient for the astronomer, who could now ride in a chair at the Cassegrain focus.

A number of different instruments were developed at Herstmonceux for attachment at the telescope's Cassegrain focus. An 'electronographic' camera used an electronic method of light amplification to increase the telescope's ability to photograph very faint objects. Since a large proportion of the telescope's time would be spent in studying the spectra of stars and other objects, two spectrographs – one with an electronic detector – were developed for this purpose, and these became the workhorses of the INT, used much more than any other instruments. For measuring the brightness of night-sky objects, two photometers were made available. Although developed for use by the RGO's own astronomers, all these devices were also available for visiting astronomers to use. Alternatively, visiting astronomers could attach their own equipment to the telescope.

Electronic detection was still a novelty when the INT came into service. Speaking in 1967, Woolley claimed, somewhat extravagantly, that image intensification, 'if it works', would make the 98-inch INT as effective as a conventional 1000-inch telescope would be in detecting faint objects[3].

The third mode of operation of the INT, and potentially the most powerful for some purposes, made use of the coudé focus. For this, a different convex mirror was inserted near the top of the telescope, and additional plane mirrors installed to bring the light to a focus in a room beneath the telescope. These mirrors were arranged in such a way that the point of focus was always in the same place, regardless of which way the telescope was pointing. As a result, heavyweight detecting equipment no longer had to cling to the back of the telescope, but could stay in a fixed position in the coudé room. Used at the coudé focus, the INT could have produced more detailed spectra than was possible in the Cassegrain arrangement, but this was never fully achieved. The coudé room had to be sited on the south side of the telescope – the sunny side – and despite double-thickness insulation on the skin of the building, the coudé room was prone to variations in temperature which made long-exposure spectroscopy, essential when dealing with faint objects, nearly impossible. Plans were made to build a brick wall outside the dome to act as a sun shield, but these were not implemented. As a result the coudé focus was little used.

The INT did not initially make use of computer control, but a few years after it went into service a minicomputer was installed in the control cabin. This was for use in controlling the instruments attached to the telescope, and for downloading and analysing data. Its internal memory was a tiny 64 kilobytes, some thousand times smaller than that of many mobile phones today.

To work at the Cassegrain focus the observer could ride in a chair slung below the main mirror.

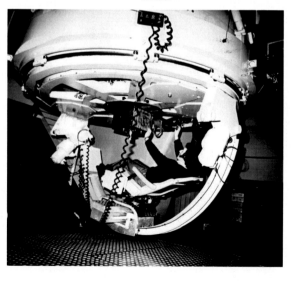

The performance of an astronomical telescope can be quantified in a number of different ways: in terms of its light-gathering power which allows it to detect extremely faint and distant objects, its resolving power which enables it to pick out tiny details, and its magnifying power which enables it to enlarge small images. The first two of these increase with the size of the primary lens or mirror, which is why astronomers strive to build ever larger telescopes. Both also depend on the quality of the optical components and on the seeing at the site concerned on any given night.

With its 98-inch mirror, the INT was capable of catching 125,000 times more light than enters a single dark-adapted human eye. Its sensitivity was further increased by using photographic detection with long-exposure times, and later by electronic means. By keeping the telescope trained on the same patch of sky for periods of an hour or more enough light could be captured to produce an image of objects which would not be detected at all at short exposure times. There was a limit to this, however, imposed by the fact that even on the darkest moonless night, the sky between the stars is not completely black. Atoms in the upper atmosphere give off a faint airglow and there is also scattered light from interplanetary dust. Local sources such as street lamps also light up the night sky, a phenomenon which became an increasing nuisance at Herstmonceux with the expansion of the nearby town of Eastbourne. The result of all these effects is to set an upper limit on the useful exposure time, which for the INT at Herstmonceux was about two hours under the best observing conditions. Nothing was gained by exceeding this limit, since the resulting image would simply become increasing fogged by the background light.

According to the User Guide to the INT,[4] the telescope was capable of photographing objects in the sky down to a limiting magnitude of 22 when used at prime focus under the best conditions. Magnitude is the astronomer's way of measuring the apparent brightness of stars and other objects. The greater the magnitude, the fainter the object being studied, with an increase of one in magnitude corresponding to a decrease of 2.5 (approximately) in the apparent brightness. On this system a bright star, easily visible to the naked eye, has a magnitude of about 1 (a 'first-magnitude' star) and a faint star at the limit of visibility to the naked eye has a magnitude of about 6. A star of magnitude 22 – the limit for the INT – is 2.5 million times fainter than anything we can see directly. Put another way, the INT was capable of detecting a 100 watt lightbulb at the distance of the moon.

The resolving power of a telescope is a measure of its ability to produce an image of two stars very close together in the sky in which they appear as separate spots of light rather than a single blur. It is limited by a fundamental property

Part of a plate exposed at the INT's prime focus, magnified by a factor of 6. Faint stars appear as tiny dots, but brighter ones become discs at this exposure. The size of the disc indicates the brightness, not the size, of the star. All these stars are much too faint to be visible to the naked eye.

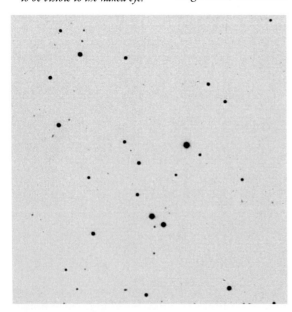

of light waves called diffraction, which becomes less and less of an obstacle the larger the telescope's primary mirror or lens. For the INT under the best seeing conditions the angle between two stars which it could just resolve was quoted as 1 second of arc (1/3,600 of a degree of angle). This is equivalent to the width of a pound coin at a distance of 2.5 miles, or of a crater 1.2 miles wide on the moon. Under the seeing conditions more normally encountered at Herstmonceux the resolving power was two or three times less than this.

Although not primarily intended for looking through, the INT was on occasions used for direct visual observation. This could be done by replacing the photographic plate-holder at the prime or Cassegrain focus with an eyepiece. With a 2-inch eyepiece at the Cassegrain focus, for example, the observer would see things magnified by a factor of 700. In some arrangements observation could be carried out even while the telescope was in use with one of its attached instruments. By keeping an eye to the eyepiece, the observer could ensure that the telescope remained precisely directed at the intended target throughout the observing run.

'When main telescope fails, break glass'. The replica of Newton's original telescope acquired an unofficial extra label after it went on display in a glass case in the INT dome.

By the time the Queen inaugurated it in December 1967, the telescope had already been tried out, though only as part of the commissioning process, and only by RGO staff. Bringing it fully up to peak performance was expected to take at least a year, so astronomers from elsewhere would not be let loose on it until the autumn of 1968. Regular use by RGO astronomers began in March of that year however. From then on, the telescope was in use every night when conditions allowed. Throughout its eleven-year period of operation at Herstmonceux, the INT would prove remarkably reliable. Only twice would it be out of action for more than a week for repairs. Most faults would be corrected in time for the next night's viewing.

Routine observing with the INT on a nightly basis was, at the least, a two-person job. Movement of the telescope, opening and closing of the dome, and its rotation, were in the hands of a Night Assistant. He (they were all men) took command of the control panel, and was responsible for seeing that the instrument came to no harm from misuse or adverse weather conditions. Night Assistants worked a two-shift rota – before and after midnight – during the long winter nights, but only one in the summer. Their presence left the other member of the team, the observer, free to concentrate on making the actual observations, working

To minimize lost observing time, maintenance work was generally done during the day. Here an engineer is working at the Cassegrain focus.

directly with photographic materials, and ensuring the telescope remained precisely aligned towards whatever astronomical object was being scrutinised. When electronic detecting equipment was used instead of photography, the observer would often be supported by additional staff to set up and run this equipment. RGO technicians were on call at night also, to minimize the loss of valuable observing time in the event of a problem with the telescope itself.

By day, maintenance engineers were on site to service the telescope and ensure it was correctly set up for the next night's observing. With many different groups using it for many different purposes, changes of configuration were a regular necessity. In 1974, for example, the year's observing yielded 671 spectra, 151 direct photographs and over 200 other observations. To make this possible, the instrumentation attached to the telescope had to be swapped round 57 times, and there were a further 38 end changes, in which the optical arrangement was altered to move the focus point, where observing was done, from the top end of the telescope to the bottom, or vice versa. In addition, the primary mirror had to be removed and re-aluminised three times during this period. All this took a lot of manpower. Operating, maintaining and updating the telescope and its accompanying equipment was estimated to require the full-time efforts of 16 members of the RGO staff.

The observers who used the INT were either locals from the RGO or visiting astronomers from other institutions which had been allocated time on the telescope. The latter could hire bedrooms in the North Attic of the Castle for less than a pound a day, and could also order packed midnight meals from the canteen. RGO observers simply drove in from home, or even, when the weather was uncertain, waited there until summoned by phone by the Night Assistant.

To prepare for their night's work, the assistant and observer, and any support staff, entered the building by a small door on the north side, and made their way up to the dome by lift or stairs. The highest level, 48 feet above ground, gave access to the telescope itself. The control console was on this level, as were toilets, a kitchenette and a rest room – important when so much time was spent waiting for the clouds to part. To allow easy checking of sky

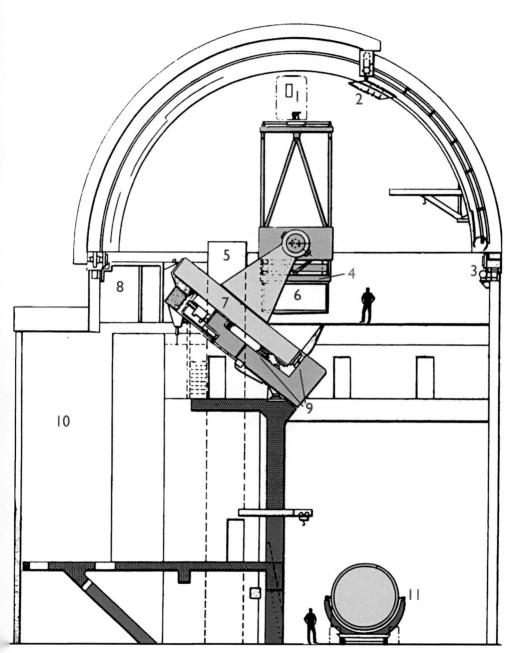

Scale drawing of the telescope and its building at Herstmonceux. KEY: *1 – observer's cage (prime focus);
2 – crane for raising and lowering the main mirror; 3 – machinery for rotating the dome; 4 – 98-inch mirror;
5 – lift shaft; 6 – Cassegrain focus; 7 – polar disc; 8 – dark rooms; 9 – oil bearing pads; 10 – coudé room;
11 – mirror aluminising plant.*

conditions, there was a walkway running round the outside of the building, reached by a small door from the observing floor.

For astronomers working with photographic materials, there were darkrooms leading off the observing floor. Great pains were taken to coax the best possible performance from the photographic plates used on the telescope. To this end, special fine-grain astronomical plates were used which were stored under chilled conditions and then put through a process called hypersensitisation shortly before use. This was a recently-devised technique (some called it black magic) in which the plate was baked, usually in an atmosphere of nitrogen, at about 60°C for several hours shortly before use. Equipment was available in the dome to do this. Hypersensitised plates were two to three times more sensitive than untreated ones when used to record faint objects. As a result exposure times at the telescope were reduced, allowing the astronomer to obtain more images in the course of a night's work.

The INT control desk in 1974.

For astronomers used to working alone in unheated domes in the depths of winter, conditions at the INT were comparatively luxurious. Much of the actual observing was done at the main focus – the Cassegrain focus – seated on a chair which could be moved on a frame so that, whatever the angle of the telescope, the observer remained nearly upright. And when not actually needed at the telescope observers could retreat to the control room and benefit from the heat output of the equipment there.

Astronomers were not the only people allowed into the INT dome. The telescope had been bought with taxpayers' money, so arrangements were made to allow members of the public to inspect the instrument they had paid for – though only during the day. Astronomers and visitors were strictly segregated, with the latter entering by a separate door at ground level. They then had to climb the 64 steps of an enclosed spiral staircase to reach the level of the Observing Floor and enter the glazed viewing gallery where they were rewarded with a splendid view of the telescope.

Improvements were made to the INT during its years at Herstmonceux, mainly in the form of new detection equipment, but also to make the telescope easier to control and operate. As early as 1968 tests were done to see if there was any advantage in attaching a TV camera to the INT's viewfinder, which was an 8-inch refractor mounted on the main telescope. This meant that the Night Assistant and observer could see on monitor screens exactly where the main telescope was pointing.

An exterior walkway round the dome allowed observers to step outside to check sky conditions at night, and also affords a rooftop view of Herstmonceux Castle by day.

Deciding who should use the telescope, and how much observing time they should be allocated, was a sensitive issue, since bids for observing time outstripped supply. Observing time during the darker periods when moonlight did not interfere, was in particular demand. The job of adjudicating between rival claims was given to a 'Large Telescope Users Panel', which apportioned time on the INT and on a second telescope managed by the Science Research Council, the 74-inch Radcliffe reflector in South Africa. In the INT's first year of operation the Panel awarded two seven-night observing periods to astronomers from the Royal Observatory, Edinburgh, while those from the universities of London, Oxford, Cambridge and Dunsink received an average of nine nights each. The remaining observing time was given to the RGO. In later years the proportion allocated to outside observers increased to more than 50 per cent and a wider range of outside institutions was involved.

In January 1969 the Royal Astronomical Society held one of its regular meetings in the lavish new premises of the Royal Society in London's Carlton House Terrace. In the chair was the society's president, Donald Sadler. For the benefit of younger members, he recalled that nearly 23 years had elapsed since the Society, under his predecessor as president, Harry Plaskett, had first proposed the erection of a large telescope in the United Kingdom. Sadler himself had been a secretary of the Society at that time, and played an important role in the early campaign, and it was a great pleasure to him to invite the Astronomer Royal to speak. 'The Isaac Newton Telescope', began Sir Richard, 'works very well indeed, and despite the climate we have done a good deal with it'.[5]

Through the long gestation period, it must have been easy for the astronomers involved in the project to forget that the ultimate purpose of the Isaac Newton Telescope was to further mankind's understanding of the universe. Now, after years in which it had sapped the time and energy of engineers and astronomers, the telescope was at last beginning to give something back.

6 Exploring Sussex skies

IN ONE WAY the telescope's long gestation period worked in its favour. By the time it finally entered service in the late 1960s, the science of astronomy was moving into a new and exciting phase. The universe had sprung a few major surprises in the preceding two decades, and astronomers would want to use the new instrument to try to answer questions that simply would not have been asked back in the 1940s. Indeed some of the objects they would study with the INT were completely new to science, undreamed of when the project began.

In Britain the post-war renaissance had begun with the construction of new radio telescopes: the huge steerable dish at Jodrell Bank, and a number of large-scale arrays – groups of smaller aerials linked together and often movable on rails – constructed near Cambridge. These instruments picked up faint radio emissions from objects in the sky, and much ingenuity was used to pin down the positions of these radio sources as precisely as possible. Because they are so large, radio telescopes can be extremely sensitive, capable of detecting very faint emissions from remote parts of the universe. By the mid-1960s one of the telescopes at the Mullard Radio Astronomy Observatory (as the Cambridge establishment was now called) would reach further into the universe than any other instrument in the world. Its development would help two of the Cambridge pioneers, Martin Ryle and Anthony Hewish, to win the 1974 Nobel Prize for Physics, the first astronomers ever to be honoured in that way.

The emergence of radio astronomy made new demands on optical astronomy too, as researchers sought to discover what, if anything, was visible in the sky at the points where radio sources had been discovered. Many of the sources turned out to be

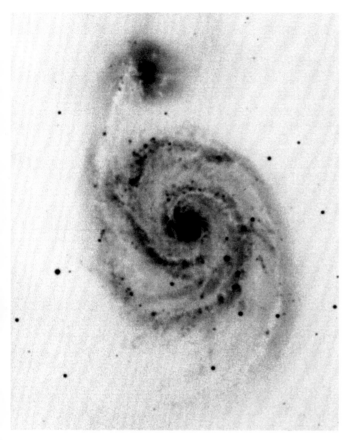

Astronomers often worked directly with the plates exposed on their telescopes, which are photographic negatives, rather than with prints made from them. This is part of a plate exposed on the INT in 1970, showing the 'Whirlpool Galaxy', M51. This galaxy is also an emitter of radio waves (see also page 141).

associated with distant galaxies visible in optical telescopes, but other sources were more puzzling. These were eventually found to be associated with a totally new class of bluish starlike objects, known first as quasi-stellar radio sources, and later as quasars. By the early-1960s the number of known quasars was increasing rapidly, but they remained puzzling objects.

At this time it was accepted by most astronomers that we live in an expanding universe, where distant galaxies are receding from us at a rate that increases in proportion to their distance away. This recession manifests itself through the Doppler effect, a change in colour of the light received from the galaxy, known as the redshift. It can be measured with a spectrometer attached to a telescope, which effectively serves as a speedometer to measure the rate of recession (or occasionally approach) of whatever object is being studied.

When this technique was applied to quasars, surprising results were obtained. From studies of the way their light was redshifted it seemed likely that quasars were extremely far away – billions of light-years from Earth. (For comparison, the limit of the observable universe is about 14 billion light-years away.) If quasars are really that far away, then they must be intrinsically extremely bright in order to be visible at such a distance. Some individual quasars were calculated to be 100 times brighter than an entire galaxy of 100 billion stars.

Yet studies carried out by Herstmonceux astronomers using their smaller telescopes before the INT came into service showed that quasars could vary markedly in brightness over comparatively short periods. This was work in which the RGO led the world, and in one extreme case a twenty-fold flare-up in a quasar's brightness was found that lasted a few months, with fluctuations over just a few days that corresponded to a variation in its energy output equivalent to switching on and off all the stars in the Milky Way. Such rapid variation meant that whatever a quasar was, it must be a relatively small object compared to the size of a galaxy, since an object cannot change in brightness in less time than it takes light to travel from one side of it to the other[1].

Radio-telescopes could find these compact objects in the sky, but only by using an optical telescope to pinpoint an object's exact location and measure the redshift was it possible to confirm it was indeed a quasar. It is no surprise, then, that teams from both Jodrell Bank and the Cambridge radio-astronomy observatory were keen to enlist the INT in the search for quasars.

One of the earliest published results from the INT appeared in the leading scientific journal *Nature* in March 1969. Three RGO astronomers reported their findings under the title 'Optical Positions of Radio Sources'[2]. On the suggestion of Martin Ryle, very precise positions had been determined for sixteen radio sources that were of particular importance to radio astronomers. This was done by extremely accurate measurement of photographs taken with Herstmonceux telescopes, principally the INT at its prime focus. All but two of these sources are now confirmed as quasars. Results announced the following year show the INT being used, not just to obtain photographs of some recently-discovered radio galaxies, but to record their spectra.

One quasar that was studied in detail with the INT was 3C273 – a designation which indicates that it is source number 273 in the third Cambridge catalogue of radio sources, published in 1959. As seen from the Earth, 3C273 is a thirteenth-magnitude object (it varies a little) in the constellation Virgo, and like all quasars it is only visible with a telescope. It is about two billion light-years away, and emits some 2,000 billion times as much energy as the sun. 3C273 had already been studied at other observatories, but observations of its spectrum done on the INT over six nights in February and April 1974 added details that had not been detected elsewhere[3]. The team of observers was made up of astronomers from the RGO and from University College London, using a revolutionary new detector, developed at University College by Alec Boksenberg, attached to a spectrograph. This was the Image Photon Counting System (IPCS), a complex electronic device that included a photo-electric detector and image intensifier, scanned by a television camera whose output was gathered, sorted and stored in a computer memory. The IPCS was a device of extraordinary sensitivity, capable of detecting the arrival of single photons of light – the tiny lumps of energy of which light is made up. (With a loudspeaker attached to the IPCS astronomers could even listen to the irregular clicking caused by the arrival of individual photons from the quasar). Boksenberg went on to develop a version of the IPCS for the Hubble Space Telescope, and later became Director of the RGO. The IPCS became standard equipment for observatories around the world until superceded by a new generation of detectors, the 'charge-coupled devices' or CCDs.

The illustration on the right shows one of the spectra of 3C273 obtained in this research and is typical of the way astronomical results are often presented. The spectrum appears in the form of a graph. Wavelength is plotted along the horizontal axis, representing colour, which runs in this case from blue on the left, through green, yellow and orange, to red (and some

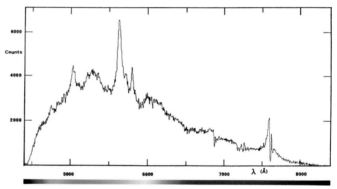

infrared) on the right. The vertical axis shows how bright each colour appears in the spectrum of this quasar. This is given in terms of 'counts', the number of clicks of the IPCS recorded in a given length of time. (For technical reasons light at the blue end of the spectrum, where the quasar is brightest, was filtered out in this observing run before it reached the detector, so the curve falls to zero at the left-hand end.) Because of the expansion of the universe, 3C273 is moving away from us at a speed of about 40,000 kilometres a second. This means its light is redshifted so that features on the spectrum plot are displaced a few centimetres to the right of where they would otherwise be. Allowance had to be made for this when interpreting the spectrum.

Spectrum of the quasar 3C273 obtained with the INT in 1974 – see text for details. Astronomical research papers abound in diagrams of this type. The coloured bar has been added here to indicate the range of colours covered by the graph.

Analysis of spectra of this sort reveals much about conditions in the part of the quasar that is emitting the light. In this study the sharp peaks are spectrum lines which indicate the presence of atoms of hydrogen, helium, neon, sodium and magnesium in 3C273. More detailed study of these lines gave clues to what processes are going on in the quasar to cause it to emit so much energy. One advantage of using the IPCS is that it made it possible to subtract out most of the background skylight which would otherwise be mixed in with the light from the quasar. In reporting their results, Boksenberg and his team also acknowledged unwitting assistance provided by the British government at the time of some of their observing runs: by imposing a regime of power cuts at a time of serious fuel shortage, the government had ensured that the skies over Herstmonceux were darker than usual.

Quasar observations continued to feature in the work programme of the INT throughout its time at Herstmonceux. Amongst astronomers at large the enigma of just what quasars are was beginning to be resolved. There was increasing agreement that quasars really are as far away as the redshift evidence suggests and that they must therefore emit prodigious amounts of energy. The idea gained ground that this energy could be supplied by gravitational collapse – the infalling of matter towards the centre of the body when there is nothing strong enough to prevent it. Gravitational collapse on a large enough scale might eventually lead to the formation of a black hole – a term first used in this context in 1968. In the following year a Herstmonceux astronomer, Donald Lynden-Bell, showed how infalling stars and gas could power a quasar as they spiralled into a Schwarzschild Throat (his name for a black hole) whose mass was at least ten million times greater than that of the sun[4]. The widely-held view today is that

Donald Lynden-Bell's diagram to illustrate his pioneering theory of the way black holes might form at the centres of galaxies, put forward when he worked at Herstmonceux in the 1960s.

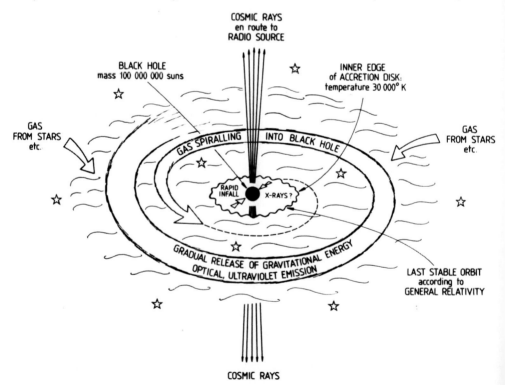

most, perhaps all, galaxies have a 'supermassive' black hole at their centre. Matter spiralling into this black hole becomes immensely hot, giving off the radiation we see as a quasar. Lynden-Bell's important contribution was later recognised with the award of the prestigious Kavli Prize in Astrophysics in 2008.

Quasars were not the only deep-sky (extra-galactic) objects studied with the INT at Herstmonceux. Another puzzling category were the Seyfert galaxies, named after the American astronomer who first drew attention to them in the 1940s. Seyferts look like normal galaxies, often showing the characteristic spiral structure, but have an abnormally bright central core or nucleus. The INT, and its spectrographs, including again the Boksenberg IPCS, were brought into play to study the spectra of a number of Seyfert nuclei. New features were found which helped astronomers work out what is going on there. Similarities with quasars were apparent at the time, and it is now generally agreed that a Seyfert galaxy is a half-way house to a quasar, probably harbouring a massive black hole at its heart. One Seyfert studied by Boksenberg and colleagues from London University and the RGO using the INT is designated NGC4151. Follow-up studies using other telescopes – on the ground and in space – eventually made it possible to calculate what the mass of the object at the centre of this Seyfert galaxy must be, by measuring the rate at which gas clouds circled around it. The result of this exercise was that the central object – presumably a black hole – is about one billion times more massive than the sun, the first time anyone had 'weighed' a black hole at the centre of a galaxy.

Moving on from quasars and active galaxies to more normal ones, we find RGO astronomers using the INT, with other telescopes, in 1973-4 to measure the redshifts of 31 galaxies in a group of galaxies in the constellation Leo known as Abell 1367[5]. Most galaxies in the universe do not exist in isolation, but belong to clusters in which the members move at high speed relative to one another, like bees in a swarm. These speeds can be found by measuring the redshifts of the individual galaxies in the cluster, and from this it is possible to calculate the strength of the gravity holding the cluster together, and hence the mass of the whole cluster. The mass of Abell 1367 turned out to be very much greater – by a factor of several hundred – than the combined masses of all the stars in all the visible galaxies in the cluster, a result that was in agreement with what had been found for other clusters. The conclusion was that there must be much more matter in the clusters than we can see in telescopes. Just what this so called missing mass consists of was unknown; rebranded as dark matter it remains an enigma today, even though it is thought that most of the matter in the universe exists in this invisible form.

Galaxy M82 in a print from part of a plate exposed on the INT in 1971. The exposure time was ten minutes.

The galaxies in Abell 1367 are more than 300 million light-years distant. Rather closer to home, though still well beyond the confines of our own galaxy is a far-from-typical galaxy called M82 – No. 82 in the catalogue published by French astronomer Claude Messier in 1781. One glance at M82 in a powerful telescope is enough to show that something unusual is going on there. By the 1950s the general opinion was that this was an exploding galaxy, racked by some cataclysmic event at its centre. Later evidence contradicted this, suggesting that M82 was a more ordinary galaxy that happened to be passing through a cloud of intergalactic dust. But this theory was overturned again in the 1970s when astronomers David Axon of the University of Sussex and Keith Taylor from the RGO turned the INT on M82. Their unexpected finding was that spectrum lines from hydrogen gas in the galaxy were split, something that could not happen if the light was being scattered by dust clouds. The conclusion, since confirmed for other similar galaxies, was that matter was indeed streaming out at high speed from the centre of M82. The exploding galaxy theory was revived in a slightly different form[6].

Today M82 is classed as a starburst galaxy, where new stars are forming at a much more rapid rate than in more normal galaxies. The process was probably triggered quite recently, in astronomical terms, when M82 had a close encounter with a nearby galaxy, M81. A super-wind of gas streams out from the newly-forming stars, and it is some of this that was detected with the INT. In a sense, M82 is an exploding galaxy after all.

The INT was not solely used for studying objects far beyond the confines of our own galaxy. Perhaps its most significant finding concerned a faint star a mere 7,000 light-years away. In December 1970 a satellite called *Uhuru* had been launched with an x-ray telescope on board, and had soon shown that the sky is peppered with x-ray sources which cannot be detected from ground level because their rays are blocked by the atmosphere. *Uhuru* gave a reasonably precise location for the second most powerful x-ray source in the sky, positioned in the constellation Cygnus and therefore known as Cygnus X-1. By the following summer, astronomers had a strong suspicion that the source of the x-rays from Cygnus X-1 was an otherwise insignificant star, visible with a good telescope, and catalogued as HD226868. At the end of July, RGO astronomers Paul Murdin and Louise Webster turned the INT on to this star and recorded its spectrum. HD226868 turned out to be a normal star of the type classified as a blue supergiant, and Murdin and Webster speculated, in a paper published in September 1971, that the source of the x-rays might not be the blue supergiant itself, but a companion to it[7]. Many stars in the sky are in fact double systems, in which a pair of stars orbit around each other, like skaters on an ice-rink, and it would not be surprising if the Cygnus X-1 system turned out to be one of these.

No companion to HD226868 could be seen, however, but there was a way in which its presence might be detected. If the blue supergiant and its companion were orbiting round one another, then at certain times the supergiant would probably be travelling towards the Earth, and then half an orbit later it would be travelling away. Such motion would betray itself through the Doppler effect, as a tiny shifting of the star's spectrum lines towards the blue followed by a tiny shift towards the red. When Murdin and Webster continued their observations at the INT between August and October 1971 they managed to find just such an effect: the blue supergiant alternated between approaching the Earth and receding at a similar speed, a pattern which repeated every 5.6 days. This left little doubt that HD226868 does indeed possess a companion. Murdin and Webster were even able to estimate that the invisible object was somewhere between 2.5 and 6 times heavier than the sun. 'It is inevitable' they wrote when they published their results in January 1972, 'that we should speculate that it might be a black hole'[8].

The type of black hole they envisaged was not the same as the supermassive black holes mentioned earlier as powering the quasars that lurk inside galaxies. This would be a stellar-sized black hole, formed when a star a good deal heavier than the sun collapses after it has finally run out of fuel – an object perhaps ten times heavier than the sun, but less than 20 miles in diameter, whose gravity is so intense that neither matter nor light can escape from it. As with the quasars, it is matter pulled into the black hole that emits the x-rays.

Murdin and Webster could not be certain they had found the first stellar-sized black hole, as there might be other explanations. But unknown to them a Canadian astronomer, Tom Bolton, was performing similar observations at the same time as theirs, using a 74-inch telescope, and reaching the same conclusion. Other black hole candidates have since been found, and most astronomers would agree today that it is highly likely that the Cygnus X-1 system harbours a black hole. (Soon after Murdin and Webster announced their discovery, the cosmologist Stephen Hawking entered into a tongue-in-cheek wager with a fellow astronomer, Kip Thorne. The issue was whether or not Cygnus X-1 would ultimately turn out to be a definite black hole. Hawking bet that it would not, but conceded defeat in 1990 in the face of mounting evidence.)

An artist's representation of the Cygnus X-1 system. The visible blue supergiant star orbits round an invisible but massive companion, perhaps a black hole. Matter is pulled off the supergiant and spirals into a disc round the companion, becoming so hot that it emits x-rays.

Stellar black holes are not the only remnants a star may leave behind at the end of its life. Some years before the Cygnus X-1 incident, another exotic class of objects had been discovered, the remnants of stars that are not massive enough to leave a black hole. As with quasars, it was again radio astronomers who led the way. In November 1967, just a few days before the inauguration of the INT, a research student at Cambridge's Mullard Laboratory, Jocelyn Bell, was using a newly-constructed radio telescope – an array of aerials covering an area of 4.5 acres – when she came across a most unusual signal. Instead of the usual hissing noise picked up by radio telescopes, something in the sky was emitting a steady series of radio pulses, more regular than the clicks of a metronome. Suspicions were soon aroused that the emitter in question might be the first known example of a type of star whose possible existence had been predicted as long ago as the 1930s, called a neutron star. In the following weeks three more of these pulsating radio sources – soon to be named pulsars – were found.

News of the discovery caused a sensation among astronomers when it was publicly announced in Cambridge at the end of January 1968, and raised the question of whether these objects gave off visible light as well, so that they could actually be seen to be flashing. Astronomers around the world were soon at their telescopes hoping to be make the first visual sighting of a pulsar. The INT had not yet been fully commissioned, but on the night of 4th February an RGO astronomer, Michael Candy, climbed into the telescope's prime focus cage to examine the patch of sky where one of the pulsars was said to be. A flashing object as faint as 16th-magnitude would have been visible, but he saw nothing. Photographs taken on the INT also drew a blank, as did those taken on one of the smaller Herstmonceux telescopes using a technique of interrupting the incoming light with a rotating blade to improve the chance of detecting anything flashing at exactly the predicted rate.

Astronomers at other observatories were equally unsuccessful. Optical detection of a pulsar proved much harder than anticipated, and despite a number of false alarms, was not achieved until a year later, when an American team succeeded using a more sophisticated TV-based observation technique. The original suspicion that pulsars are neutron stars within our own galaxy was confirmed. They are star remnants that have collapsed to form a hard sphere less than thirty miles in diameter, made of tightly packed neutrons – a material so dense that one cubic centimetre of it can weigh up to a billion tonnes. Because the star is highly magnetic, the radio waves it emits are channelled into a beam that sweeps across the sky as the star rotates, in the same way that the beam from a lighthouse scans round the horizon. A pulsar pulsating once a second, for example, is evidence of a neutron star rotating once a second, its radio beam sweeping past the Earth once each rotation.

Some stars, on the way to becoming a neutron star or black hole, suffer a massive explosion in which matter is thrown out into space. When this happens, the star becomes a supernova, its brightness increasing by a billion times or more. Other stars – the lighter ones – evolve less dramatically into small dense, still-glowing remnants known as white dwarfs. Even a white dwarf can explode under certain circumstances, becoming what was known at that time as a Type I supernova, and blowing itself out of existence in the process. Detailed study of these events, in which a previously unnoticed star flares up enormously over a period of a day or two and then subsides over the next few weeks, yields much information of value to astronomers.

Supernovae appear without warning. They are rare in our own galaxy but can be observed in other galaxies. To glean as much

A fine view of galaxy M33 printed from a plate exposed on the INT at Herstmonceux. The exposure time was 15 minutes. M33 is one of the closest neighbours of our own galaxy, about 3 million light-years distant. The remnants of old supernovae have been detected in this galaxy.

information as possible, astronomers need to start their study of a supernova as soon as it is spotted – ideally before it has even reached its maximum brightness – and continue their observations as it subsides over the next few weeks. Since observing time on the INT was allocated months in advance, RGO astronomer Roger Wood was granted an 'override facility' which allowed him to take over the telescope at short notice when a suitable supernova appeared, provided its current users were prepared to forego part of their allotted observing time.

The discovery of new supernovae was disseminated worldwide by telegrams, automatically printed out at Herstmonceux on a Telex machine in the typing pool. Outside office hours it was the duty of the Observatory's night-watchman to check this machine at regular intervals and contact Wood by phone if a message arrived. More often than not the galaxy in which the event had occurred was not visible from Herstmonceux and no action was needed. But in April 1974 a supernova appeared on the outskirts of a distant galaxy catalogued as NGC4414 which happened to be well-placed for observing from northern latitudes. Wood and a colleague, Bruce Patchett, immediately began a study which started just before the supernova reached its peak brightness and continued, with help from some of their colleagues, as it faded over the following eight weeks. Over this period they managed to measure the supernova's brightness on 21 occasions, and recorded its spectrum 12 times. Because NGC4414 is so far away, the supernova, subsequently named SN1974g, only reached 12th magnitude at its peak, much too faint to be seen with the naked eye. It then faded to 15th magnitude by the end of the study.

It is likely that processes taking place during a supernova explosion lead to the creation, out of lighter atoms, of atoms of many of the heavier chemical elements. The spectra obtained from SN1974g, for example, carried the signature of materials such as iron, magnesium, silicon and titanium. Atoms of these and many other elements found in the Earth probably originated in material blown out into space by supernova explosions that took place in an earlier generation of stars, before the solar system formed. Patchett and Wood also found evidence of a shell of debris blown out from SN1974g at about 10,000 kilometres per second, like a three-dimensional smoke ring[9].

Measurements of the peak brightness of a type 1 supernova, such as those obtained by Patchett and Wood for SN1974g, are important in cosmology because they provide a way of measuring the distance of remote galaxies. Even before the eruption of SN1974g astronomers knew enough about the process that causes a Type 1 supernova eruption to deduce that all such supernovae, wherever they occur, must have the same intrinsic brightness. Patchett and a colleague at the RGO, David Branch, had even worked out what this brightness must be: Type 1 supernovae at their brightest are always, in round figures, 300 billion times brighter than the sun. So if all such supernovae are actually equally bright, one that looks very faint must be very far away, while one that looks brighter must be closer. In principle, the distance to NGC4414, the host galaxy of SN1974g, could be found simply by measuring how bright the supernova appeared in the sky, as Patchett and Wood had done.

(Two decades after the eruption of SN1974g, Patchett and Wood's results were again put to use. By then the Hubble Space Telescope was in action. From its vantage point above the atmosphere it could be used to measure the distance to NGC4414 by a new, more reliable method involving the study of a special type of variable star in the galaxy called a Cepheid. Armed with this independent distance measurement, an American astronomer, Bradley Schaefer, used Patchett and Wood's measurements, together with those of other astronomers who studied SN1974g, to work out a value for the universe's rate of expansion. From this he estimated the age of the universe – the time that has elapsed since the universe came into being at the Big Bang – to be around 15 billion years, remarkably close to the modern accepted value of 13.7 billion years.[10])

Sixteen months after the appearance of the NGC4414 supernova, another interloper appeared in the sky without warning, and the INT was again pressed into service at short notice to observe it. This time the object in question was not a supernova but a nova – a stellar eruption less violent than a supernova but in this case bright enough to be clearly visible to the naked eye.

The nova was spotted first by amateur astronomers in Japan on the evening of Friday 29th August 1975. As night fell in Britain a few hours later, astronomers familiar with the night sky also noticed that something was wrong in the constellation Cygnus. A familiar pattern of stars had been augmented with a bright new one. That evening the INT, with other telescopes at Herstmonceux and around the world, was turned on the newcomer, which was still increasing in brightness at that time. By the Saturday night the nova had reached second magnitude, placing it among the 50 brightest stars in the sky as seen from the Earth. Its sudden appearance, and the fact that the INT was following its progress, was reported in the national press. The nova soon faded, however, and by the Tuesday evening had lost 95 per cent of its brilliance, becoming invisible to the naked eye soon afterwards.

Nova Cygni 1975, as it was called, was the second brightest nova of the twentieth century. A star that was hitherto barely detectable even with the largest telescopes, had suddenly flared up to a million times its normal brightness. This happened because the star in question, V1500 Cygni, is actually a binary consisting

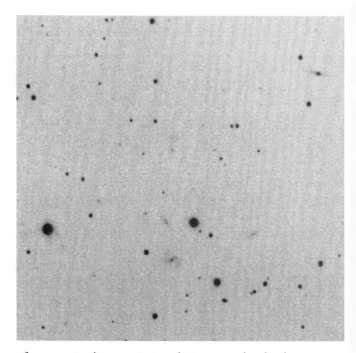

Peering into deep space: at least four distant galaxies appear as faint smudges amongst nearby stars in this small portion of a plate exposed on the INT at Herstmonceux.

of two stars in close proximity orbiting around each other every 3.3 hours. One of these is a white dwarf, and when hydrogen gas from its partner falls onto the surface of the dwarf it causes a flare-up. The result is the nova we observe. The star is not destroyed in the process, and V1500 Cygni is likely to flare up again in a few tens of thousands of years. Nova Cygni 1975 appeared so bright because V1500 Cygni is a star within our own galaxy, just a few thousand light-years away – compared with more than 50 million light-years for the supernova mentioned earlier. Later evidence has shown that V1500 Cygni is a rare type of double star, in which the white dwarf has an extremely strong magnetic field.

Many different astronomers used the INT as a research tool during its eleven-year active life at Herstmonceux, publishing their findings in nearly 100 papers in the scientific journals. Just a few of the results of more general interest have been described here. Later evaluation would show, as we will see, how much more the telescope could have achieved had it not been so severely handicapped by its location.

The work described in this chapter makes another important point. Apart from the discoveries that were (or sometimes weren't) made with it, the availability of the INT at Herstmonceux played a vital part in another key aspect of astronomical progress – the development of instrumentation. The intimate connection between instrument development and practical astronomy was apparent in Michael Candy's early attempt to detect an optical pulsar. Its failure revealed the weakness of the instrumental activity at the RGO at that time – its dependence on traditional engineering methods. The RGO attempt to detect the pulsar relied on a rotating mechanical vane, whereas the later successful attempt in America made use of more modern TV techniques.

By the time Murdin and Webster were measuring the motions of Cygnus X-1 – the black hole candidate – a new instrument known as the spectracon was being developed for astronomy at the RGO by Dennis McMullan. Murdin and Webster had access to this detector as part of its testing phase, and it was this that gave them the opportunity to monitor Cygnus X-1 over a long enough term to discover its 5.6-day period of oscillation. In this case the astronomical results proved more impressive than the performance of the spectracon, whose significance was to fade with the arrival of the IPCS.

In developing the IPCS as a modern detector in the 1970s, Alec Boksenberg could move back and forth between his laboratory in London and the INT, feeding his experiences with the telescope back into further improvements in the lab. (Logistically this was no easy task, since the equipment had not yet been engineered into a compact form. The gang of scientists who transported it back and forth became known as 'Boksenberg's travelling circus'.) In more ambitious exercises Boksenberg also took his equipment to the 200-inch telescope on Mount Palomar. He acknowledged that the weather in California was superior to that in Sussex, but also that the INT experience had played a crucial part in his own intellectual development from an instrument scientist to an astronomer. Within a decade Boksenberg would be Director of the RGO, and only under his leadership, building on that of his predecessor Francis Graham Smith, would the RGO's instrument development programme become fully competitive.

7 Troubled times

THE WEATHER in the months that followed the entry into service of the Isaac Newton Telescope was notoriously wet – though not much worse than the Astronomer Royal was expecting. Writing in *Nature* at the time of the inauguration Sir Richard predicted a figure of 40 per cent for the proportion of nights that would be clear enough for some work to be undertaken with the new telescope – a figure based on meteorological data from the Herstmonceux weather station, and on the experience with other instruments at Herstmonceux, some of which had been in use for nearly twenty years. In the event, in the sixteen months following the inauguration in December 1967, some observing was possible on just over one-third of nights (39 per cent). But only fifty nights in the whole period were completely clear. In the observing log despairing descriptions such as 'watched the guide star slowly disappear into the murk' were all too common.[1] The frustration was particularly intense for visiting astronomers who travelled from some distance to use the telescope. Even though they were encouraged to apply for considerably more observing time than they actually needed, it was not unknown for them to return home at the end of their allocated period without even seeing the dome opened, and faced with a three-month wait until their next opportunity. The RGO astronomers suffered too of course, though it was easier for them to get on with other things (or stay in bed) while waiting for the sky to clear. One of them, Roy Wallis, with a gift for cartoons, amused his colleagues with a drawing in which huge fans had been installed on the outside of the dome to blow a hole in the clouds above.

No-one had expected that Herstmonceux would be a good site for a world-class telescope. Now it was becoming apparent just how bad it was. It was not just the number of cloud-free hours that was disappointing, the clarity of the air even when there were no clouds was deficient too, limiting the telescope's ability to detect faint objects. Light pollution from the expanding metropolis of Eastbourne was another problem. Compared to Herstmonceux, it was reckoned that a really good overseas site could provide three times as many viewing hours and an order of magnitude improvement in the telescope's sensitivity. (To be fair, later years at Herstmonceux were not as bad as 1968. In 1974, for example, observing was possible on two nights out of every three, and one night in six was completely clear.)

The doubts that many in the astronomical community felt about the siting of the INT soon spread to the wider scientific arena. The telescope had barely been in operation a year when an editorial appeared in *Nature* referring to the 'now widespread belief that it may, after all, have

'O.K. IT DOES BLOW THE CLOUD AWAY, BUT WE STILL CAN'T USE IT'

Blowing the clouds away: RGO astronomer and cartoonist Roy Wallis offered a new solution to the problem of cloudy skies.

been unwise to lavish a large amount of money' on a telescope in the 'somewhat doubtful seeing conditions of the Sussex coast'.[2] This was followed a few weeks later by another suggesting it might be time that 'the charade being played out on the Channel coast of Sussex' should come to an end. 'Why not take the plunge', it continued, 'and move the Isaac Newton to a better site ...?'[3] So by June 1969 the seeds of the idea had been sown.

At this time the wider question of the availability of British telescopes in the Northern Hemisphere came under review. (The Southern Hemisphere would be adequately catered for when the 48-inch UK Schmidt and the 150-inch Anglo-Australian Telescope came on stream in 1973 and 1974 respectively.) A 'Northern Hemisphere Review Committee' (NHRC) was set up to advise the Science Research Council, who held the purse-strings, on what resources it should provide for British optical astronomers in the Northern Hemisphere. The Astronomer Royal was a member of this group, and at a meeting in November 1969 he was asked about the possibility of moving the INT. Sir Richard replied that he 'did not think a case existed' for moving it, and pointed to evidence which suggested that moving a telescope cost roughly as much as providing a new one.[4] (In this, as we shall see, he was right.)

The NHRC was not a happy committee. Its deliberations were described as full and frank, code for long-winded and acrimonious. Part of the problem was the presence at most of the meetings of two astronomers, described as 'overseas consultants', who though British by birth had moved to work in the United States – part of the brain drain that at one stage saw some two thousand British scientists emigrating every year. The intention was that if the views of expatriates could be accommodated in the plans for better facilities for UK-based astronomers, the brain drain might be stemmed or even reversed. One of these expatriates was a British theoretical astronomer then based in California, Geoffrey Burbidge, a large, loud man described by his wife as

Light pollution was an increasing problem at Herstmonceux. In this time-exposure the INT dome is silhouetted against the skyglow produced by the nearby town of Eastbourne.

not suffering fools gladly, by himself as a gadfly, and by a senior government scientist as very abrasive. With two other expatriates (one of them his wife, who was also an astronomer), Burbidge tabled an inflammatory paper for the NHRC which delivered a full-scale attack not just on the INT but on the RGO also. The INT, it said, in its present location was 'not merely ineffective but useless', while it would be 'folly' to go ahead with a new large Northern Hemisphere telescope 'if any part of its development or operation is to be put in the hands of the present RGO'.[5] Not surprisingly, Woolley objected both to the pejorative reference to the RGO and to the idea that the RGO should not be involved with the proposed new observatory.

Stalemate ensued, with the committee dividing into two camps: on the one hand the chairman, the brilliant and colourful Cambridge astronomer Fred Hoyle, together with the younger university-based researchers, and on the other those pillars of the astronomical establishment, the Astronomers Royal. Hoyle had little time for the RGO's astronomers, who seemed, he observed, to be more concerned about their pension rights than the research possibilities of a new telescope, and he made no secret of his disdain for the RGO itself, an institution which in his view was well past its sell-by date.

The future of the INT would be tied up with the conclusions reached by the NHRC, but despite the best efforts of its chairman, the committee was unable to put forward any unanimous proposal. There was general agreement that some degree of reorganisation in UK optical astronomy was essential, and that universities should be given more money for research, an elaborate calculation having shown that the astronomers of the Royal Observatories appeared to be unfairly favoured in this respect. More importantly, there was unanimous agreement that a new Northern Hemisphere Observatory (NHO) should be provided, urgently and definitely not sited in the UK. But on the question of how that observatory might be set up and run no agreement could be found. A majority of the committee favoured the establishment of an entirely new body to do the job, a National Institute for Astronomy (NIA). The two Astronomers Royal were implacably opposed to this. In their view the NIA – a 'monolithic government institution' with an estimated staff of more than seventy – was wholly unnecessary when more direct, less costly, and more traditional methods were readily available.

The NHRC report, with a dissenting Appendix from the Astronomers Royal, was delivered to the Science Research Council at the end of 1970, but was never published. When, where and how the NHO should be set up, if at all, would remain uncertain for several more years. When the stalemate was finally broken, it would be the Astronomers Royal who were proved right. Britain never would have a National Institute for Astronomy.

The early 1970s were a time of turmoil in British optical astronomy, which was widely seen as being in decline and in need of revival. Uncertainty about the Northern Hemisphere Observatory was one cause of discontent. The appointment of a successor to the Astronomer Royal was another.

Sir Richard Woolley retired from the post of Astronomer Royal and Director of the Royal Greenwich Observatory at the end of 1971. His successor was none other than Margaret Burbidge, wife of the Geoffrey Burbidge mentioned above, and a signatory to the provocative paper put to the NHRC in 1969. She was a British-born astronomer who early in her career had worked at another ill-sited observatory, the University of London Observatory at Mill Hill. (On one occasion during World War 2 she had been part of a team who continued observing at the 24-inch reflector there even as two Flying Bombs exploded nearby in quick succession).

Margaret Burbidge had worked in the United States for many years. With her husband and two other astronomers, Fred Hoyle and William Fowler, she had co-authored in 1957 a ground-breaking paper describing how chemical elements are formed inside stars. She had gone on to make a name for her observational work on galaxies and quasars, and had become the first woman astronomer ever elected a Fellow of the Royal Society. Against her own better judgment Dr Burbidge agreed to return to Britain to run the RGO despite, in her own words, 'not having the temperament to direct a major scientific establishment',[6] and believing, wrongly, that the observatory would almost run itself while she continued her researches at telescopes around the world. Her tenure at Herstmonceux would be brief and unhappy.

The staff at Herstmonceux were unhappy too, because Margaret Burbidge was only appointed to run the observatory, without the title of Astronomer Royal. For the first time since its founding in 1675 the Director of the Royal Observatory would not also carry the prestigious royal title. There was a valid argument for this: why should not a radio astronomer, a theoretician, or even an x-ray astronomer, become Astronomer Royal, even though leaders in these fields might not be best-qualified to run the optically-based RGO? So in 1972 the position of Astronomer Royal was given to the radio-astronomer, Sir Martin Ryle, and was never again held by a serving Director of the RGO.

Margaret Burbidge found herself at the head of an institution that was divided: a younger generation of researchers who couldn't wait to get the INT moved to a better site, and an old guard, unionised and steeped in the mores of the Civil Service, who were bitterly opposed to the idea. And all felt slighted because they no longer had an Astronomer Royal at their head. The scientific staff had petitioned the Queen to prevent this happening, and would go on to protest to the Prime Minister, but to no avail.

Meanwhile the row about the siting of the INT in Sussex rumbled on. In 1971, *Nature* called it 'the most short-sighted decision in the management of British astronomy', and reported that many astronomers now saw the observatory (not just the INT) as a white elephant.[7] Matters came to a head a year later, and again it was Geoffrey Burbidge who stirred things up. Writing from California, he sent a 1,200-word letter to *Nature* in which he described British optical astronomy as third rate, and listed eight key mistakes which, he thought, had brought this about. The INT was top of his list – siting it in the UK had rendered it 'almost completely useless'[8] – but there were many other problems too. (Another expatriate astronomer, Wallace Sargent, disagreed with Burbidge. British optical astronomy, he thought, was not third-rate; it was fourth-rate.)

Nature *pronounces on the state of British astronomy in September 1972.*

Scandalous Muddle in British Astronomy

THE letter in *Nature* from Professor Geoffrey Burbidge last week (**239**, 117; 1972) has brought into the open   this, and the University of Ca zealous among them.

Burbidge's tirade enraged many in the astronomical community and placed his wife, as Director of the RGO, in a difficult and embarrassing position. When *The Times* reported on the Burbidge letter a few days later, the article was headed 'Leading astronomer may go to US'. 'Dr Margaret Burbidge', it said, 'is expected to return to the United States if a crisis in British Astronomy is not resolved soon'.[9] There was, said *Nature* in a bold headline, 'Scandalous Muddle in British Astronomy'.[10]

Even the Prime Minister, Edward Heath, was concerned. He

had read the *Times* article, with its news of 'what seemed to be incomprehensible decisions about the siting of telescopes', and wanted to know what was really going on.[11] The government's Chief Scientific Adviser, Sir Alan Cottrell, took soundings and reported back. The Burbidge letter contained some truths, but also half-truths and misleading statements. British optical astronomy was on the whole third-rate by the standards of the big Californian observatories. The INT was certainly badly sited and a move was being considered. But it was by no means 'almost completely useless', and was currently doing some first class work on distant galaxies. As to the Burbidges, Sir Alan thought that since Geoffrey had turned down various senior positions offered to him in the UK and returned to the USA, his wife would want to rejoin him there.

At least someone's smiling!

At a time when morale was particularly low among RGO staff, spirits were raised by the site of a smiling INT dome – victim of one of the practical jokes traditionally played by each year's intake of vacation students.

In the event, Margaret Burbidge stayed another year, resigning in September 1973. She had been Director of the RGO for just 16 months. In the mean time controversy had flared again after *The Times* published an article headlined 'Britain too cloudy for new £1m telescope'.[12] It introduced a lengthy report in which Margaret Burbidge was quoted as admitting that the telescope would ultimately have to be moved. The suspicion that £1 million of taxpayer's money had been squandered, reinforced by Burbidge's talk of squabbles in the ranks of British astronomy, which she found 'quite repugnant', was beginning to give the whole sorry affair the whiff of a public scandal.

The row finally erupted into the correspondence columns of *The Times* at the end of January, in the form of a brief but indignant letter from a Mr W. Bates of Cheltenham. 'Who', he asked in reference to the INT, 'was responsible for this disgraceful waste of public money? What action is being taken against them?'[13]

A number of letters appeared in response to this. In the view of Ray Lyttleton, now Professor of Theoretical Astronomy at Cambridge, the villains of the piece were the 'big noises' who had swatted down lesser folk who dared to point out the deficiencies of the Sussex site. 'The unsuitability of the site was fully realized in astronomical circles at the time', he wrote, 'but it was nevertheless inflexibly decided that the telescope was going to be where it is and nowhere else almost entirely for prestige sake'. Dissenters had been 'persuaded to remain silent by assurances that any question as to the site would mean losing the telescope altogether'.[14] It was Herstmonceux or nothing.

Another reply, from the writer P. Lancaster Brown, attempted to justify the siting of the telescope on the basis of the meteorological data available when the decision was made to move the RGO to Herstmonceux back in the 1940s. What the writer did not know was that the Burbidges had by now trawled back through the INT observing books to tot up the number of hours when the dome of the INT had actually been open in its first three years. The resulting figures only served to confirm what a bad site Herstmonceux was, with only 500 to 800 clear hours per year – an average of around two hours a night and less than half what had originally been hoped.

A third respondent was Professor Michael Seaton of University College, London. Pointing to the value of the INT in giving fledgling astronomers the chance to use a large telescope and to develop new forms of instrumentation, he attempted to sweep away the opposition with a blunt assertion that 'no-one who has studied the problem carefully seriously suggests that the INT should be moved'.[15]

A comment in *Nature* that Mr Bates of Cheltenham had not received a satisfactory answer to his questions turned out to be premature. Geoffrey Burbidge had yet to react, and when his letter arrived from California a few weeks later, he placed the blame for building the telescope in Sussex squarely, and perhaps unfairly, on the shoulders of 'officials of HM government'. Who these officials were he did not say, though he did admit that they had been acting on the advice of 'senior astronomers in the United Kingdom'. He now called for the INT to be 'moved to a good site very quickly'. Proposals to do so were being soft-pedalled, he claimed, for fear that if money was spent on moving the INT, there might not be enough left to build the Northern Hemisphere Observatory.[16]

Even from the distant vantage point of the early 21st century, the question 'Could the INT realistically have been anywhere else?' still hangs in the air. That the new telescope should be set up within the UK had been implicit in the venture from the start. How could a telescope intended to revitalise British astronomy be put anywhere but where British astronomers could easily get at it? Writing in 1945, Roderick Redman thought it quite possible that foreign travel would become extremely expensive and remain 'hedged about with vexatious restrictions'.[17] In the event, as we now know, the opposite happened. But no-one could have foreseen at that time how astronomy would eventually be transformed by the advent of affordable air travel, making it quite feasible for British telescopes to operate in Australia, Hawaii, or the Canary Islands.

If the telescope was to be in the UK, then for administrative convenience Herstmonceux was the obvious place to put it. But many of the reasons why the Herstmonceux estate had been selected for the observatory – its size, convenience of access from

London, possibly even the appropriateness of a mediaeval castle as HQ for such a venerable institution – were quite irrelevant to the needs of a 100-inch telescope. For that, atmospheric conditions were paramount. Spencer Jones had maintained that the Sussex site was about the best available in Britain. What he could not know, at a time when the first transistor had yet to be created, was the extent to which developments in electronics would put new demands on telescopes. To get the best from a new generation of sensitive detectors, astronomers would push telescopes to their limits, striving not just for perfect optics but for perfect atmospheric conditions too. Nor, perhaps, should we expect astronomers in the 1940s to have anticipated how much there was waiting to be discovered in the distant regions of the universe that only telescopes at the very best sites can penetrate.

The decision to locate the INT in Sussex may possibly have made sense, on astronomical grounds as well as political, at the time it was taken, but it would appear more and more perverse as the years went by and large new telescopes began to appear at much more favourable sites around the world. From the start there had been doubters in the astronomical community. Even Harry Plaskett, in the Presidential Address that helped to set the whole project in motion, had to work hard to find convincing arguments that Britain was the right place for a large telescope. Few can have been won over by his suggestion that poor sites actually required the biggest telescopes because those were the ones that could make best use of the brief spells when the clouds parted.

Redman was one of the early sceptics. Even before the project was launched in the 1940s he had written of the folly of putting telescopes at a place with 50 good nights a year when they could have been put where there are 250. 'Astronomers nowadays know perfectly well that this is a ridiculous practice', he added, 'yet they often acquiesce, because the choice is between a new instrument in a bad situation or no new instrument at all'.[18] A year later, exactly what he feared had happened to the INT – but was there any realistic alternative? The belief that it was 'Herstmonceux or no telescope' persisted throughout the project and is still heard today. It does seem unlikely that Spencer Jones' powers of persuasion would have convinced Treasury officials in 1946 that they should finance an overseas telescope, particularly one linked to the name of Isaac Newton. But was this still the case ten years later, when Richard Woolley took over, or in 1960 when the Board of Visitors reviewed the siting question?

Woolley had observed with telescopes in California and South Africa, and can have had no illusions about how much worse Herstmonceux was going to be. Yet he firmly adhered to the 'Herstmonceux or no telescope' doctrine. He even managed to convince a sceptical Fred Hoyle (who had welcomed the INT project at its inception in the 1940s but would later describe the telescope as a 'little runt of an instrument')[19] that carrying on as planned was the least bad option. A later Director of the RGO, Francis Graham Smith, writing in 1983 denied that there had ever been any possibility of siting the telescope elsewhere, and there is no evidence that Woolley ever actually enquired of the Treasury whether funding would still be available if it were decided to build it overseas[20]. One cannot help wondering whether Woolley might indeed have wanted, as some have suggested, to keep the telescope at Herstmonceux for reasons of personal prestige. Such a powerful instrument was a fine adornment – the jewel in the crown of the unique establishment that was his personal fiefdom. No other astronomer lived in a mediaeval castle within walking distance of one of the most powerful telescopes in the world.

Further evidence of how much the telescope had suffered from its poor location was hardly needed, but came anyway in 1983 in the form of a lengthy research paper in a journal called *Social Studies of Science*.[21] Its authors were John Irvine, a sociologist, and Ben Martin, a physicist, from the University of Sussex. They were developing a means of quantifying how well or badly big science facilities performed and had used the INT as a test case. This meant comparing its performance with that of three American institutions with roughly similar telescopes. Several different methods were used, in the hope that although each method might have limitations on its own, the combined effect would mean something. To no-one's surprise, the INT came out very badly. The total number of research papers it gave rise to each year was five times lower than any of its competitors. The impact of those papers, measured by the number of times each was referred to in subsequent papers by other scientists (a method known as citation analysis), was also less than the others. In addition about 50 astronomers, including some from the RGO, were asked to place a number of different observatories in rank order, in terms of how well they felt each one performed. The INT managed to come 11th of 12, beating by a hair's breadth the only Russian observatory on the list.

Irvine and Martin's research also looked into the question of whether the INT had served any educational function. Before the telescope came into service, Richard Woolley stressed that while its main function would be to give the British astronomer of the future the chance to 'get right inside the problems of contemporary observational astronomy'[22], it would also serve as a training ground for young astronomers. It might even act as bait to tempt young British physicists to take up optical astronomy. The same idea had been in the minds of the telescope's founding fathers, and was reiterated by the Queen at the Inauguration Ceremony when she expressed the hope that the presence of the INT might help reverse the brain drain. Irvine and Martin reported the views of astronomers who had actually used the INT at Herstmonceux. Asked about its educational value they were sceptical. Disillusionment was a more likely outcome when young observers found themselves robbed of their valuable telescope time by inclement weather. (To his credit, Woolley did much in other ways to foster the younger generation of astronomers, principally by setting up the annual Summer Vacation courses which ran at the observatory from 1956 onwards. By 1975 it could be claimed that almost all the astronomers in the country aged under 40, and a few foreign ones, were former RGO Vacation Students.)

Predictably, Irvine and Martin's findings were not well received. *Nature* ran an editorial headlined 'A sledgehammer cracks an apple' in which it questioned the value of an exercise which merely added 'an air of scholarly respectability' to views that were already widely held.[23] The response from Francis Graham Smith, former Director of the RGO, was more robust. He objected strongly to what he called 'tendentious nonsense' in the paper, in the form of innuendoes about the observatory and the competence of its staff. One factor alone was sufficient to account for the telescope's meagre output: the Sussex weather.[24]

Another question also lingers: 'Why did it all take so long?'. If the telescope had been ready in eight or ten years instead of 21, the decision to keep it in Britain would have seemed much less perverse.

From the start the INT project was hampered by a lack of clearly-defined leadership. As *New Scientist* magazine pointed out in 1972, optical astronomy in Britain had for many years lacked a personage of the stature of Lovell and Ryle in radio astronomy or Hoyle in theoretical astronomy – a list from which the names of Spencer Jones and Woolley are noticeably absent.

Yet Harold Spencer Jones is said to have been the most gifted of all the Astronomers Royal, and an outstanding administrator as well as astronomer. But little was achieved in the decade when he chaired the telescope's Board of Management. He was a man of great integrity; aware that the INT was not to be part of the Royal Observatory, he would not have wished to give the impression that he was taking it over. Yet if the Astronomer Royal was not the 'owner' of the INT project, then who was? Only when the Science Research Council took over the RGO from the Admiralty in 1965 did it become clear exactly who was running the INT.

For ten years, the Board of Management failed to reach agreement about the design of the telescope. Even where acceptable solutions already existed, as for the problem of making the 'tube' sufficiently rigid, money and time were squandered following up novel alternatives which in the end were dropped. A kindly critic has described these ideas as 'ahead of their time'. Not surprisingly, potential users of the telescope grew impatient. The members of the Board of Management were mainly establishment figures in British science, their role akin to that of non-executive directors on the board of a company – though in this case it was a company without a full-time Managing Director, and one in which the shareholders, the astronomers who would actually use the telescope, had no voice. Rightly or wrongly the perception developed, and persisted throughout the project, that the older generation thought they knew best and the views and suggestions of younger astronomers were not welcome.

Practical experience in building and using large telescopes was in short supply in Britain at this time – hardly surprising since that was why the INT was needed in the first place – and advice from any quarter should have been welcomed. The hugely experienced firm of Grubb Parsons was already turning out 74-inch telescopes for a number of overseas observatories, and would surely have taken a direct request for a larger one in its stride. Hindsight suggests that had the Board gone to Grubb Parsons at the outset and placed an order for a straightforward 100-inch reflector, they might well have received an instrument of much the same quality as the one they eventually did get, but at lower cost and in less than half the time.

Concurrently with the INT, Spencer Jones was involved in another, much greater, project, one for which he certainly did have full responsibility: the revival of the Royal Observatory after the ravages of the War, and its re-establishment on the new site in Sussex. Projected to take one or two years, the move took ten and like the INT was still incomplete when Spencer Jones retired in 1955. He had much to contend with. In the austerity days of the late 1940s, the RGO was seriously short of experienced staff, and there was nowhere for them to live in the Herstmonceux area. Money was tight and all expenditure subject to the penny-wise procedures of public accounting. He also had to deal with local planning issues and the concerns of worried locals.

In the face of all these difficulties, Spencer Jones had soldiered on. The complexities and frustrations involved in the two simultaneous ventures would have broken a lesser man. It is to his credit that the RGO's move to Herstmonceux was eventually judged a

The local paper, the Evening Argus, *announces the closure of the INT – two months after it actually happened.*

EVENING ARGUS, Monday, May 14, 1979 **15**

Giant eye on the sky sleeps . . .

It's Operation Shut down

Left: parts of the dismantled INT are lifted out through the dome, following the closure of the telescope in March 1979. Above: the same scene in 2007.

success, while his crucial role in initiating the INT project should not be forgotten, even if the venture made little headway under his chairmanship. Only in Spencer Jones's very last month in office did things begin to move, with the setting up of an Executive Committee to drive the project along.

Throughout the years of controversy and recrimination, planning and negotiation, the Isaac Newton Telescope continued in operation at Herstmonceux. By the mid-1970s it was clear that its days were numbered at this site, and a sort of planning blight descended as plans for improvement and updating were put on hold and eventually abandoned. Finally, in March 1979 the telescope took its last look at the skies of Sussex. It had been in full operation there for less than eleven years. Engineers from Grubb Parsons travelled down to dismantle it, and the pieces were hoisted through the open dome for lowering to ground level, ready to be shipped back to Newcastle where the telescope would be improved and altered. The dome itself was left intact, but with the nightly observing routine discontinued and the telescope gone, the heart had gone out of it. Its only function now was to serve as a distinctive landmark for shipping in the English Channel.

The status and prospects of the RGO were diminished too. The departure of Herstmonceux's flagship instrument would eventually be seen as a pivotal moment in the history of Britain's national observatory.

The 98-inch mirror is lowered into the crate where it will remain for more than 20 years.

The telescope in its dome on La Palma in 1985. To accommodate the change in latitude, the polar disc is now 21° closer to the vertical than it was at Herstmonceux.

Part Two

'Above The Grosser Clouds'

THE TELESCOPE ON LA PALMA

Telescope domes along the ridge on La Palma. The Isaac Newton is second from the right.

8 Moving on

THROUGH THE TROUBLED YEARS of the early 1970s, there was one ray of hope for British observational astronomers: the Science Research Council had pencilled into its long-term planning a substantial sum not just for a new telescope, but for a whole new observatory. Despite the failure of the Review Committee to produce an acceptable blueprint for the way British astronomy was to be run, the idea of a Northern Hemisphere Observatory had not disappeared from view, and a new committee – the NHO Planning Committee, again with Hoyle, initially, as chairman – had been set up to carry forward the detailed planning that would be needed.

The new committee was keen from the start to avoid the sort of problems that had bedevilled the INT project two decades earlier. At its first meeting in July 1971 one member warned of the dangers of becoming sidetracked by the possibility of incorporating untried technical innovations into the design of the telescopes, as the original INT Board of Management had been. Another member urged the appointment of a 'Project Officer' right from the start, something the original INT had not had. The new Committee would heed both these warnings, though not perhaps as positively as their proposers had wished.

Part of the Planning Committee's brief was to specify the suite of telescopes the NHO should be equipped with. Their conclusion was that the mainstay of the new observatory should be a reflector designed for observing the faintest and most remote objects in the universe. Its primary mirror would be as large as was practicable and affordable at that time, 177 inches in diameter (more conveniently expressed as 4.5 metres in the metric units then coming into fashion). This was later reduced to 4.2 metres (165 inches). To support the main instrument the observatory would be equipped with two other telescopes, one of about 2.5 metres (98 inches), mainly to be used for spectroscopy, and a smaller one of 1.0 metres (39 inches). When a detailed specification for the middle one of these was drawn up, it was clear that a suitably upgraded INT might well fit the bill. The telescope had been one of the world's largest when new, but by the standards of the 1970s it was merely a medium aperture instrument. In 1972 Margaret Burbidge, who was on the NHO Planning Committee, had reiterated her view that money was being wasted by keeping the INT in Britain and that moving it should be seriously considered. Soon the committee was requesting its estimators to work out what it would cost to upgrade the telescope and move it to the NHO, wherever that might be. When the result showed that this would be £1.5 million cheaper than buying a new telescope, and would take three years less time to achieve, the case for reusing the INT was beginning to look a strong one.

By 1974 there were two important new players on the scene. The first of these was Professor Sam Edwards, a Cambridge physicist, who took over as Chairman of the Science Research Council in late 1973. It was clear to him that in a situation where bids for research funds greatly exceeded what was available, setting up a new independent organisation to run the NHO project would be an unwarranted extravagance. So financial stringency finally resolved the stalemate from the Northern Hemisphere Review Committee; Britain could not afford a National Institute for Astronomy as well as a new observatory. Responsibility for the NHO project would have to go to an existing organisation. The option of saving money by moving the INT must have looked attractive also.

The other new arrival was the radio-astronomer from Jodrell Bank, Francis Graham Smith, who joined the staff at Herstmonceux as Director-Designate in 1974. Following the Burbidge debacle, the Directorship of the RGO had gone – to the disappointment of many – to a safe pair of hands, Alan Hunter, a seasoned administrator in his sixties who had been with the observatory for 36 years. Graham Smith was destined to become Director when Hunter retired at the end of 1975.

At its 16th meeting, in November 1974, the NHO Planning Committee heard that the SRC had agreed in principle its main proposals, namely that there should be a Northern Hemisphere Observatory with the three telescopes as planned, and that one of these should indeed be the upgraded INT. Furthermore the organisation to be given responsibility for the project was the RGO, under its Director-elect, Francis Graham Smith. More than anyone else it was he who would bring the new observatory into being.

The RGO Tercentenary Sundial in the grounds of Herstmonceux Castle commemorates the anniversary in 1975 which was also the occasion when future plans for the INT were announced.

In the summer of 1975 the Royal Observatory celebrated its three-hundredth anniversary with a series of special events. *Nature* marked the occasion with specially-commissioned articles. It was in one of these, by Graham Smith, that the news that the INT was to have a new home was first made public.[1] By a pleasing, if fortuitous, symmetry, the telescope whose original conception had been announced at one tercentenary, that of Isaac Newton, was given a new lease of life at another. (Less happy, in view of what was to follow for the RGO, was the title chosen for Graham Smith's article: 'The next 300 years'.)

For British optical astronomers this was a key moment. The big new Anglo-Australian telescope was just coming into service in New South Wales, where the UK Schmidt instrument was already in use. Now they were to have a whole new observatory in the Northern Hemisphere too, at an estimated cost of £13 million – nearly £100 million in 2009 terms. It was a turning point for the staff at Herstmonceux also. For the first time in its long history the Royal Observatory had been given a new primary purpose. Some would be sorry to relinquish their traditional role and lose their flagship telescope, but others were glad to embrace the new and inspiring challenge they had been given: to set up, equip and run, for the benefit of all British astronomers, a brand new world-class observatory. Just one thing remained to be decided: where exactly was the new observatory going to be?

Fittingly, it was Isaac Newton himself who first suggested where astronomers should go to find the best sites for their telescopes. Writing in 1717 he pointed out that no telescope could 'take away that confusion of rays which arises from the tremors of the atmosphere' – a remark that shows he was fully aware that it is atmospheric turbulence that makes the stars twinkle and produces poor seeing for astronomers. He went on to propose a possible remedy. 'Most serene and quiet air' might be found, he suggested, 'on the tops of the highest mountains, above the grosser clouds'[2].

More than a century passed before Newton's suggestion was put to the test. In 1856 the Astronomer Royal for Scotland, Charles Piazzi Smyth, was given a grant of £500 by the Admiralty to mount an expedition to Tenerife in the Canary Isles. The aim was to set up a temporary high-altitude observatory, in order to 'ascertain how far astronomical observation can be improved by eliminating the lower third part of the atmosphere.'[3] Tenerife had been chosen because its 12,000-foot central peak was largely accessible by horse or mule.

With his wife, his assistants, a 7-inch refractor 11 feet long, and sundry other measuring instruments, Smyth sailed to Tenerife in the private yacht *Titania*, kindly made available by its owner, the engineer Robert Stephenson. On arrival they climbed to 8,900 feet with the aid of 20 horses and mules, and set up what Smyth called a 'residence above the clouds'. A variety of observations, by day as well as by night, were carried out from this station over a period of about a month. They then moved even higher, to 10,700 feet, for another month.

The results were spectacular. 'The stars shone brilliantly,' Smyth reported, '... and caused the dome of the skies to appear resplendent with glory.' With the telescope he could see stars that were four magnitudes fainter than could be managed with the same instrument in Edinburgh. It was not just the lack of cloud and the clarity of the air that made the difference, the steadiness of the images was also much improved. Stars that were 'amorphous figures' in Edinburgh now appeared as 'clear little disks surrounded by regular rings'. (Smyth was probably seeing the diffraction-limited image, which is the best any telescope can produce.) The expedition had indeed found the 'serene and quiet air ... above the grosser clouds' that Newton predicted. As they set sail for home, the party looked back at the island's peak and wondered 'how long the learned world will delay to occupy a station that promises so well for greatly advancing the most sublime of all the sciences'.

Piazzi Smyth's telescope on Tenerife in 1856, with the mountain peak beyond. The telescope's stand was made of wood filled with stones.

The virtues of the Canarian sky were not entirely forgotten over the following century. In 1910 a French astronomer was there to study Halley's comet, while in 1959 astronomers from around the world converged there to study a total eclipse of the sun. Other scientific expeditions to the Canaries followed, but it was not until 1964 that Spanish astronomers set up what would go on to become one of the world's first international observing sites, the Observatorio del Teide, on the slopes of Tenerife's central peak. (The summit itself was unsuitable because of the corrosive volcanic vapours emitted there.)

Back in Britain, the Northern Hemisphere Review Committee had recommended that a systematic search for a site for the NHO in the Mediterranean area should begin in 1970, well before the observatory itself was expected to receive even a provisional go-ahead. The job of site-testing was to be shared between the two Royal Observatories, but soon devolved onto one of them only, the Royal Observatory, Edinburgh (ROE) under its director Hermann Brück. He was Astronomer Royal for Scotland – the post once occupied by Piazzi Smyth – and was the person who in 1967 had first proposed that British astronomers should have a new observatory.

Astronomical site testing was by now a serious business, far removed from the days in the 1930s when Spencer Jones toured the country estates of southeast England looking for a new home for the RGO. For the new generation of telescopes with their sophisticated detecting equipment, only the very best observing conditions would be acceptable, and with the advent of cheap air travel, astronomers could scour the globe to find them.

Research elsewhere was showing that first-rate sites were few and far between. The first requirement was, of course, that a telescope could actually see the sky – an absence of cloud for as much of the time as possible. Satellite data indicated that this would be found in two belts around the Earth, from near the equator to about 40° north or south. These were also the regions which have the maximum number of hours of darkness around the year. Britain lies well outside these zones. Since much cloud forms as a fairly low-lying blanket, a mountain high enough to allow a telescope to stand above this layer was another prerequisite.

Most important is that elusive quality, good seeing, that is only found in places where, as Newton realized, the air the telescope will look through is steady and devoid of turbulence. Dry, stable air should flow evenly across the observing site, something that only reliably happens over or near the sea in just five areas of the world, all of them on the western side of major oceans. Conveniently, these are also places where the air is clearer than it is over continents, and such dust and haze as exists tends to be trapped at low levels by what meteorologists call a temperature inversion. Add to this the threat of light pollution, which implies little or no human habitation or activity in the vicinity of the observatory, either now or in years to come, and the site requirement becomes even more stringent.

For the NHO three sites were initially considered, in Italy, Southern Spain and Tenerife. First results from the Italian site were not encouraging, while Tenerife was rated good but not first rate. In Spain no testing was possible because the authorities had not allowed access, ostensibly because the necessary data was in their

Map showing five regions of the world where first-rate observing conditions are to be expected, as proposed by the American astronomer Merle Walker and his colleagues in 1976. Also shown are the sites of four of the world's leading observatories today:
a – La Palma, Canary Islands,
b – Mauna Kea, Hawaii,
c – Arizona, USA,
d – Atacama, Chile.

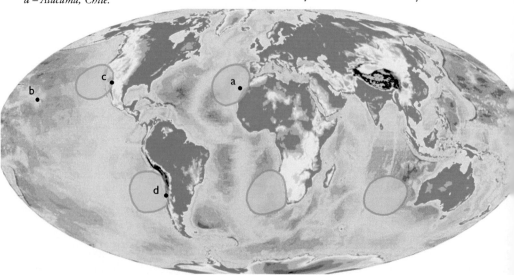

opinion already available. This was particularly worrying because another site on Spanish territory, the Canary island of La Palma, was beginning to look like a serious contender.

La Palma is one of the smaller Canary islands, lying 300 miles from the coast of northeast Africa. It was described in 1971 as sparsely populated, well off the tourist track, and its inhabitants mainly farmers. The island is in fact the visible upper portion of a volcano that rises some 20,000 feet from the sea bed. The land springs steeply out of the sea, with the highest ground near the northern end of the island. Here there is a caldera – a six-mile wide eroded crater, now a national park. The highest point, on the rim of the caldera, is the Roque de los Muchachos, or 'Rock of the Lads', so-called from the rock formation there which looks slightly like a huddle of people.

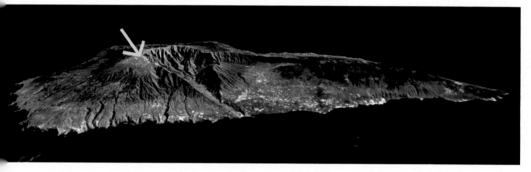

In April 1971 two astronomers from the RGO called in briefly at La Palma and came back with positive reports. They walked up to the Roque, where they reckoned astronomical site-testing would be difficult, but possible. They even enquired about the cost of building a road to the summit and were reassured by the answer. They concluded that it was 'clearly very important to examine in great detail the possibility of a site on the island of La Palma'.[4]

Serious site testing for the NHO on La Palma began in August of the following year and went on for seven weeks. For the two ROE astronomers involved, Dr Gough and Mr Heath, it was unusual and demanding work. Equipment and supplies could only be transported part way up the mountain by Land Rover. From there it was a two or three hour scramble over a desolate landscape of volcanic rock and ash to the top, with everything carried on the backs of men or mules. Tents were pitched and a base established, not at the Roque itself, but on a lesser peak on the rim of the caldera nearby, called Fuente Nueva. This was chosen in the belief, subsequently proved correct, that the streamlined shape of the mountain, combined with the prevailing northeast wind, would produce a less turbulent flow of air across the site there than at the Roque itself.

A view of La Palma from the west. The arrow shows Fuente Nueva, on the rim of the caldera, where site testing began in 1972 and the INT would eventually be sited.

Site testing on La Palma in 1972: a caravan of site testers, support staff and mules makes its slow way up to the summit. This team, not from the UK, were testing to see if the site was suitable for a specialised telescope to study the sun.

The principal task for Gough and Heath was to measure the quality of the seeing at Fuente Nueva, using a technique known as the Polar Trail method. To do this they constructed a very firm base from concrete blocks and local rocks cemented together and mounted a telescope on it so that its primary lens was 13 feet above ground. The telescope, borrowed from an American observatory, was a 6-inch refractor with an additional magnifying lens, firmly fixed to point to the pole star. Because this star is not exactly at the north pole of the sky, it traces out part of a small circle as the Earth rotates in the course of a night. Gough and Heath took a ten-minute photographic exposure once every hour during each suitable night, each exposure recording the appearance of a short length of the star's trail at the time concerned. When the seeing was good, this trail would be a narrow line, but in poor seeing it would be wider and less even. These measurements were supported with frequent observations of the wind and temperature at Fuente Nueva.

The NHO Planning Committee were expecting that La Palma would turn out to be the best site they had tested, and Gough and Heath's results seemed to confirm this. But a further full year's testing would be essential to make certain, and to reveal any seasonal variations. Before this could begin a serious problem arose which was not astronomical, but diplomatic.

Members of the Committee had been concerned that the Spanish authorities, known to be 'very touchy', might react badly to the fact that site testing had started on La Palma without their consent, even though it had been carried out with the co-operation of staff from La Laguna university on Tenerife. Diplomatic relations between Britain and Spain had been frosty for some time, the bone of contention being Gibraltar. Spain had ceded this tiny territory to Britain in 1713 but was now asserting a claim to have it back. The British government was committed to obeying the wishes of the people of Gibraltar, and they had recently voted overwhelmingly to stay British.

The Committee's concerns were well founded. The Spanish authorities got wind of what was going on on La Palma, and before the site-testing had got very far the SRC had to order the testers off the island forthwith, while the British Embassy in Madrid tried to get official permission for what they had been doing. By early 1973 it was clear, however, that if a formal application were made for further site-testing on La Palma, the Spanish authorities would turn it down. A flurry of diplomatic activity ensued, with even the Foreign Secretary, Sir Alec Douglas Home, briefed to discuss the issue at a meeting with his Spanish opposite number, though in the event he was not able to do so. Soon the British Ambassador in Madrid was so sure that any further approach would receive a 'dusty answer' that he declined even to raise the matter with the Spanish authorities for fear of souring relations even further.

Proponents of the NHO were in despair. After a tempting glimpse of what looked like one of the world's best observing sites, they now couldn't get their hands on it, even for testing and still less for actually building an observatory. In the words of a senior official at the Science Research Council, they had lost 'whatever glimmer of hope we still had about a Spanish site for the NHO'.[5] It was time to start looking for somewhere else to put the INT and the rest of the new observatory.

One possibility was another Atlantic Island, Fogo in the Cape Verde Islands, where the Portuguese authorities would actively welcome a site-testing team. But the results soon showed that there was too much haze, caused by dust blown over from the Sahara desert. And in any case the island's central peak was still actively volcanic. Another Portuguese island, Madeira looked more promising and a site-testing team was despatched there later in 1973. (A request from the Premier of Antigua in the West Indies that his island be considered had to be rejected because there is no high enough mountain there.)

One further site in a completely different part of the world was also tested. This was Hawaii, where the Americans were setting up an observatory at the top of the island's highest mountain, Mauna Kea. There was no doubt that this would provide a superb view of the sky, but there were serious disadvantages. The altitude, 4,200 metres (14,000 feet), meant that astronomers going there would need to acclimatise at a lower level to reduce the risk of altitude sickness, and must be ready for ferocious weather conditions at the summit. And because Hawaii is 11,000 km (7,000 miles) from Britain, setting up and running an observatory there would cost 25 per cent more than at a European site. Mauna Kea had already been chosen as the site for another planned British telescope, the 3.8-metre (150-inch) UK Infrared Telescope, for which the high altitude was a decisive advantage, since the additional height would take the telescope above the infrared-absorbing water vapour that exists even in clear air. Despite its drawbacks Mauna Kea would go on to become one of the world's leading astronomical enclaves, with 13 instruments sited there by 2008, including the 8-metre Gemini North reflector in whose development RGO staff played a major role.

By early 1974 there were signs of a thaw in relations between Britain and Spain and informal discussions began, not between diplomats, but between scientists, including for Britain the Chairman of the SRC, Sam Edwards, and for Spain his opposite number, the Jesuit priest Antonio Romana. A 'road map' was devised which would eventually lead, it was hoped, to a resumption of site-testing on La Palma. First the project should become a joint one between Britain and Spain, and second the British presence should be diluted by involving other European countries. This 'Europeanisation' of the project was thought to be greatly to the advantage of British plans, since it stabilised the Spanish attitude. Finally it was important that the initiative to restart site-testing should appear to come from the Spanish side rather than the British. In a manoeuvre worthy of *Yes Minister*, officials of the SRC therefore drafted a letter in which the Council invited itself to co-operate with its Spanish counterpart in prospecting in the Canaries. This letter was sent out to Spain for Father Romana to sign and send back so that Britain could accept what would appear to be a Spanish invitation. The receipt of this letter back in London in July 1974 must have been a triumphant moment for those involved – though also a private one since this had been a 'softly, softly' initiative: no-one must say anything publicly until diplomatic negotiations had caught up with the scientific ones.

The move to internationalise the observatory would eventually turn out to be of great and lasting benefit to the whole project. When representatives of Britain, Denmark, Germany and Sweden met Spanish astronomers and officials in December 1974 there was more good news. If La Palma were chosen, the Spanish would build a road to the mountaintop and bring in water and electricity. Overseas astronomers would be allowed the use of the site and its facilities in return for providing training and a share of telescope time for Spanish researchers. By then site-testers were back on Fuente Nueva, now living in a hut rather than tents.

This time the testing programme would continue for a full year. A number of astronomy students took part and one of them, Rein Bakker from Holland, kept notes of some incidents from his time on the mountain. He had gone there at short notice because his predecessor, another Dutch student, had stayed only one night, apparently scared off by the goats which, although they were nominally herded by a farmer for cheese, ran almost wild. Precautions had to be taken to prevent these goats from chewing through electrical cables. Strong winds were another problem, reaching a maximum of 133 kph (83 mph) on one occasion and causing damage to equipment. The island's worst forest fire for 100 years also occurred during Bakker's stay, surrounding the base, cutting off their supply route, and putting an end to observations for several days. Fortunately it did not reach the site itself, though later forest fires did.[6]

Despite the hazards enough data had been gathered by the summer of 1975 to allow the four thoroughly-tested sites, on Hawaii, Madeira, Tenerife and La Palma, to be compared on equal

terms. There was hardly anything to choose between Hawaii and La Palma on astronomical grounds, but La Palma had practical advantages.

Of all the Mediterranean sites tested, La Palma had the clearest and steadiest atmosphere, but the island had other merits too. It had its own airport, reached fairly easily from Britain, and at the north end, where the observatory was to be, the coastline consisted of steep cliffs washed by often rough seas, rather than beaches. For internal political reasons, Spain had not permitted development of La Palma, so there were few tourist facilities, and further development, with its associated light pollution, was unlikely. All four short-listed sites had been on volcanic islands, but on La Palma such activity as had occurred in historic times – including major eruption in 1949 and 1971 – had been confined to the southern end of the island. (There was laughter rather than alarm at a meeting of the Royal Astronomical Society when one astronomer said he had heard that La Palma's volcano was of the type that stays dormant for a long time and then blows up catastrophically without warning – 'like the one that devastated Pompeii'.)[7] As for earthquakes, there were sometimes small tremors centred at the south end, including in 1971 some 4,000 tremors over a four-day period, enough to drive some inhabitants into sleeping in the streets. But the continued survival of 400-year-old buildings in the main town, Santa Cruz, indicated that the telescopes were unlikely to be seriously disturbed on La Palma.

The La Palma site excels in the exceptional quality of seeing it provides, and in its freedom from light pollution (now protected by law), but it does have some drawbacks. Bad weather, in the form of cloud, strong wind, high humidity, snow or ice, reduce observing time by about 25 per cent, averaged around the year – still a huge improvement on Herstmonceux. Since the greatest reduction occurs in the winter, when nights are long, the number of clear night hours is fairly constant throughout the year. Different regions of the sky are visible at different times of year, so this means that no one region is favoured more than any other.

Site testing on La Palma in 1975. Left: the telescope and its pillar can be seen in the background, beyond various meteorological instruments. Right: a mule outside one of the huts, with a windbreak wall on the right.

Roque de
Los Muchachos
Altitud 2426 m

The La Palma observatory takes its name from the curious rock formation at the nearby summit, thought to resemble a group of people ('Los Muchachos' translates as 'The Lads'.)

Atmospheric dust can also be a nuisance in the Canaries. Every year some 200 million tons of dust are whipped up into the atmosphere by sandstorms in the Sahara desert. Some of this rises to a high altitude and in certain wind conditions can drift far out to sea – something Charles Darwin had noticed when he sailed past on the *Beagle* in 1832. The result in La Palma is that the stars can sometimes be dimmed by as much as one magnitude by high level haze, mainly during the summer months. For many types of observation this is not a problem. In any case, averaged around the year 90 per cent of nights are dust-free.

For the INT the contrast between its old and new homes could hardly be greater. In La Palma it would be 2,300 metres (7,500 feet) above sea level. The comparable figure at Herstmonceux was a mere 50 metres (160 feet). No other major telescope in the world was at such a low altitude. If further evidence was needed about the merits of moving the INT, it came in 1975, when an astronomy professor from Imperial College reported that his team, in their study of galaxies, had collected as much data in one month at a well-sited observatory in the Arizona desert as they managed to acquire in a year and a half at Herstmonceux.

With the site chosen and the money allocated, RGO astronomers could start to plan their new observatory in detail. But the tricky task of sorting out the complex diplomatic niceties would proceed at a glacial pace, and three more years would pass before all the signatures were in place. Along the way, a whole suite of acronyms was created to describe the agreements and structures brought into being: IGC (the Inter-Government Convention), IIA (the Inter-Institution Agreement), CCI (Spanish for International Scientific Committee), and IAC (Spanish for Astronomical Institute of the Canary Islands), which was the new Spanish organisation that would actually run the ORM (Observatorio del Roque de los Muchachos). To help defray the cost of the British plans, Holland and Ireland were brought in as partners who would also have a share of the observing time. Sweden was keen to set up its own telescope on La Palma, and other countries followed. By the time it was all sorted out Britain's proposed Northern Hemisphere Observatory had evolved into something rather different, and in many ways better: now it would be one component – admittedly a major one – of an international establishment, run by the host country, Spain, for the benefit of astronomers from many European nations. (The IAC, with the ORM and its smaller sister observatory on Tenerife, would eventually become known by yet another acronym, the ENO – European Northern Observatory.)

Plans that would allow the Isaac Newton Telescope to move to its new site were finally set in stone when all the international agreements were signed on La Palma on 26th May 1979.

A telescope transformed 9

AT LONG LAST the brakes were off. Planning and design work had been under way at Herstmonceux for five years, and within weeks of the new observatory finally receiving the go-ahead in May 1979, contracts were let for the construction of the new INT building and the dome that would sit at its top. Apart from a few dirt tracks and goatherds' caves, the observatory site was still a bare and rugged mountaintop. Reaching it from sea level on La Palma involved 20 minutes on a twisty tarred road followed by another hour of bad dirt track. Nevertheless, by the end of 1980 the main frame of the INT building was beginning to appear on the skyline at Fuente Nueva.

Staff from the RGO began moving to La Palma in the autumn of 1981. Initially they would be involved in installing and commissioning the telescopes, and would be staying long enough for wives and families to move out too. Accommodation was provided by the observatory in houses and flats on the lower slopes of the mountain, and a tiny English school was set up, with the four RGO children accounting for more than half the initial places. For secondary education it was necessary to go as a weekly boarder to the English School on the island of Gran Canaria. Soon there were plans for a British team to enter La Palma's five-a-side indoor football league, and before long there was an Anglo-Spanish marriage. These were exciting times for the RGO staff involved, though possibly even more

The new building for the INT under construction in the early 1980s.

challenging for the wives, uprooted from their Sussex homes to an island where few spoke English and the entire population is less than that of Eastbourne.

By mid-1982 the INT building was nearly complete, and Patrick Moore came to La Palma to report on progress for his *Sky at Night* television programme. At the end of the year the telescope's new main mirror arrived on the island, and soon it, and all the other parts of the INT, were making their slow way up the mountain in 18 large packing cases, the heaviest weighing 7.5 tons. There was still no tarred road all the way to the observatory, but at least there was now mains electricity there.

The complex task of putting the telescope together and getting it working would occupy the next two years, until in mid-February 1984, almost five years after it closed down at Herstmonceux, the INT was ready for 'first light' at its new site – astronomers' term for the moment when stars are first seen through a new telescope. A television news crew was in attendance for the occasion, and a report was aired on ITV's *News at Ten*. On the first night, stars were 'seen' through the telescope by a TV camera mounted at the prime focus position. By the fourth night, video-recordings obtained of some of the night sky's finest sights – the Orion Nebula, the Crab Nebula and galaxy NGC4151 – were so good that the First Night Team awarded themselves a private celebration with an early-morning bottle of Spanish brandy. The largest telescope on European soil was back in business.

The smallest telescope in the Isaac Newton Group, the 1.0-metre Jacobus Kapteyn reflector, saw 'first light' on La Palma a few weeks after the INT.

A few weeks later the INT was joined on the mountaintop by another of the three telescopes planned for the Northern Hemisphere Observatory, when first light was reached on the 1.0-metre Jacobus Kapteyn telescope (JKT), named after a Dutch Astronomer well-known for pioneering studies of the Milky Way in the early twentieth century. The third and largest member of the group, the 4.2-m William Herschel Telescope (WHT) was under construction by Grubb Parsons in Newcastle but would not come into service for another three years. When completed it would be the third largest single-mirror telescope in the world.

Later that year it was decided that the name of Isaac Newton should be attached not just to the one telescope on La Palma but to the whole group. Paul Murdin, the RGO astronomer in charge on La Palma at the time and a man intimately involved with the new observatory over many years, explained the reason for the change: 'In the 1960s Britain's biggest telescope was named after the British scientist most highly regarded in the world. Now in the 1980s its best collection of telescopes continues to commemorate this man'.[1] So the cluster of instruments that includes the INT was renamed the Isaac Newton Group (ING), and as such it has been known ever since, with its three component telescopes abbreviated to WHT, INT and JKT.

So by the end of 1984 Britain had a functioning Northern Hemisphere Observatory, albeit now a shared venture with the Netherlands, and under a different name. In addition to the two telescopes of the Isaac Newton Group three smaller instruments were by then in operation at the Los Muchachos observatory: two of them Swedish and the third the specialised Anglo-Danish Carlsberg Automatic Meridian Circle (financially supported by the famous Copenhagen brewery).

INT image of the Crab nebula, one of the first objects viewed with the telescope in its new home.

Back in England, progress on La Palma was being relayed to the other RGO staff through their in-house news sheet *Gemini*. 'The Roque is indeed an exceptionally good astronomical site', it reported in July 1984.[2] In his year-end message to staff, the Director, Alec Boksenberg, pointed out that this had been an exceptional year for the RGO, but also one of great upheaval. On the plus side, operations had started on La Palma, with the INT now 'working very well and delighting its users with some excellent results'. With its new instrumentation, the telescope was 'recognised as being superb'.[3] Against this, for the RGO as a whole, there had been a swift and swingeing round of enforced staff cuts resulting from the severe financial problems of its paymaster, now the Science and Engineering Research Council. These were painful at the time and a portent of worse to come.

People who knew the INT from its time in England would feel quite at home when they saw it in its new home. The telescope itself looked little changed, and the stained wood floor and dome furnishings, typical of the other RGO telescopes in Sussex, gave it a slightly old-fashioned appearance. Two lesser telescopes – the finder and the guider – that had been used at Herstmonceux were still attached to the main one (and remain so to this day though long disused). The mounting of the telescope was little changed also, though now set at a rather more dramatic angle. The new location is 21 degrees of latitude further south than the old one and as a result the massive polar disc to which the telescope is attached and whose surface has to be parallel to the Earth's equator, had had to be tilted to a more vertical angle and re-stabilised by

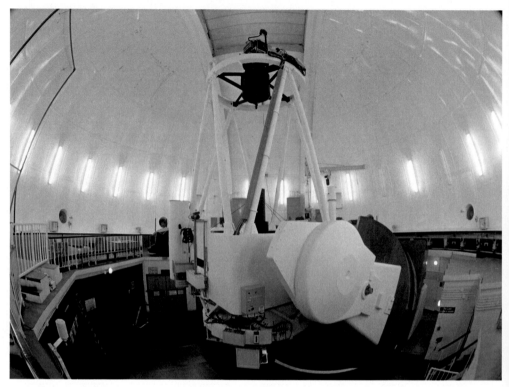

A wide-angle view of the INT and its dome in 2003.

The initials 'RGO' on a drain cover: one of the ways in which the INT building on La Palma preserves a record of its origins.

bolting lead weights at appropriate place to counterbalance the telescope structure. In its new position the disc would obstruct the telescope's view of the low southern sky, so a portion of it had to be cut away. It was not the method anyone would have chosen for mounting a telescope at this latitude, but the alternatives would have cost too much.

But a closer inspection would soon reveal that this was the INT transformed – not a transplanted relic designed in the 1950s but a state-of-the-art 1980s telescope incorporating the latest improvements in technology. Optics and electronics had moved on dramatically in the intervening decades. Gone was the cramped and uncomfortable cage at the upper end of the telescope into which observers had had to clamber to take photographs at the prime focus position. Soon to disappear too was old-fashioned photography, with its paraphernalia of glass plates, chemicals and darkrooms, which had been the mainstay in the early years at Herstmonceux. On the new INT everything could be done by remote control, and the Prime Focus Camera would use CCD technology – the now-familiar digital camera system. For attachment at the lower end of the telescope – the Cassegrain focus – RGO engineers had developed a range of new spectrographs and detectors so that visiting astronomers could draw on whatever would best suit their needs.

The most fundamental change to the telescope – the optical equivalent of a heart transplant – involved the primary mirror. When the INT was dismantled at Herstmonceux, the main mirror was not sent to Grubb Parsons with the rest, but was crated up and placed into storage. (It would eventually return to Herstmonceux and go on permanent public display at the Observatory Science Centre.) To make best use of the much improved site a better primary mirror was essential, one that would reduce one-hundredfold the problems that had arisen at Herstmonceux from uneven heating and cooling of the original Pyrex mirror. So a new mirror had been ordered, some years earlier, from the leading German glass-making firm of Schott, and ground, polished and figured by Grubb Parsons in England.

The new 2.54-metre (100-inch) Zerodur mirror being inspected during the polishing process at the Grubb Parsons works. The polishing tool has been raised above the mirror.

The new mirror is slightly larger than the original one, 100 inches in diameter (2.54 metres) instead of 98 inches (of which only 96 were actually used), and was no longer made of Pyrex. The increase in size meant that the telescope would now capture slightly more light, but the change of material was much more significant. Schott had developed in the 1960s a remarkable 'zero-expansion' material trademarked Zerodur, which does not expand or contract to any appreciable degree when heated or cooled, and this was used for the new mirror. Zerodur is an example of a glass-ceramic material. It appears reasonably transparent to the eye, but is actually made up of glass in which a huge number of tiny beads of crystallised glass are immersed, each less than 1/10,000 of a millimetre in size (the ceramic component). The normal glass expands when heated, but the crystals have the opposite property, contracting as their temperature rises. By getting the mixture just right it is possible to produce a material in which the two effects cancel out – a zero-expansion product which is excellent for telescope mirrors (and incidentally for the glass-ceramic hobs in millions of kitchens). Because of this lack of expansion, Zerodur mirrors do not require the long annealing process, and can be shaped and polished much more quickly than normal glass. It has become the material of choice for many of the world's very largest telescopes, including the 36 hexagonal segments which make up the primary mirror of the 10.4-metre GranTeCan reflector which now stands a few hundred metres from the INT at the Los Muchachos observatory.

As part of the move, new mechanisms had been developed to drive the telescope and control its position with increased precision. Where it was pointing could be seen on a screen in the control room, fed from an improved low-light video camera on the finder telescope. And of course there were new computer systems,

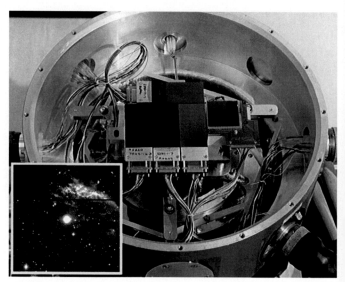

Instruments and detectors used with the INT on La Palma – 1: Interior of the Wide Field Camera used at prime focus, showing the dark brown CCDs that are the electronic equivalent of a photographic plate. Inset: image of a nebula from this camera. (By taking pairs of images slightly displaced, the black lines can be eliminated.)

enabling the astronomer or night assistant to issue instructions to the telescope by typing commands and figures at a terminal, and to store astronomical data as it came from the instruments on the telescope. A weather monitor was provided so that the observer inside the dome could check the weather conditions outside.

The telescope would continue to evolve during its years on La Palma, with instruments and systems improved and updated as technology advanced. The IPCS would soon be pensioned off, displaced by the CCD technology in whose development the RGO was a leading player. CCDs would eventually reach a state where at some wavelengths 90 per cent of the individual photons of light arriving at the detector could be recorded and counted, compared with just one or two per cent for a photographic plate. This leap in sensitivity meant that by the year 2000 the INT alone could record more photons during a night's observing than all the world's large telescopes combined in 1960. A landmark came in 1997 when RGO engineers installed an advanced CCD camera at the INT's prime focus which would define the way the telescope would be used in its remaining years. It consisted of an array of four large CCDs producing images made up of about 32 million tiny squares (32 megapixels). The area of the detector was 10 cm by 10 cm (4 by 4 inches), enough to image a large area of sky, roughly the width of the full moon, in a single exposure – hence the name Wide Field Camera (WFC). Its ability to produce detailed images in which even very faint objects would register made it ideal for survey work.

The new INT building bears little resemblance to the old one at Herstmonceux. Its boxlike lower floors initially housed the headquarters of the Isaac Newton Group, with workshops, offices,

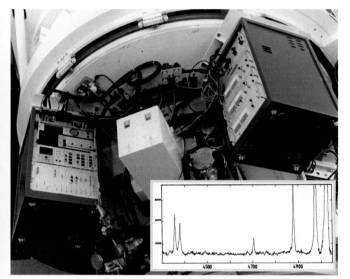

Instruments and detectors used with the INT on La Palma – 2: The Intermediate Dispersion Spectrograph (IDS) and detectors, attached beneath the mirror at the Cassegrain focus. Inset: spectrum plot from a distant galaxy obtained with this device. In recent years the IDS and WFC have been the only instruments routinely available for use with the INT.

catering and recreational areas. Until permanent facilities opened nearby, the tiny INT canteen, designed to provide midnight snacks for a few astronomers, was called on to serve three meals a day for up to 30 people working on the site.

Great care was taken in designing the building and its dome to eliminate the temperature differences that had led to trouble at Herstmonceux by producing air turbulence which degraded the seeing. The new dome and building are painted a gleaming white and insulated to keep out daytime heat. A solar screen protects them from the heating effect of direct sunlight. Asphalted surfaces outside the building are covered with white chippings, and bushes help to screen the surrounding ground from daytime heating. A ventilation system can be used to prevent the buildup of heat within the dome, and the telescope mirror can be chilled during the day to just below the expected night-time air temperature. These precautions proved successful, even though the dome itself, a hemisphere, is not of the size and shape most favoured for more recent telescopes. The William Herschel Telescope, for example, would have an onion-shaped dome.

The telescope domes on La Palma had to be much more strongly built than would have been necessary at Herstmonceux. Cloud can freeze onto the exterior of the buildings in winter, forming a thick and heavy layer of ice which adds to the load to be supported, and the wind speeds on the mountaintop are often far in excess of any experienced in Britain.

As at Herstmonceux, the telescope and the pillar which supports it were intended to be totally separate from the surrounding building, so that no vibration would be transmitted from the building to the telescope, for example when the dome is being rotated. In practice however, whether by mistake or misunderstanding by the local construction workers, the narrow air gap between the two was bridged by solidly-packed thermal insulation. This had to be removed by poking it with rods and raking out the fragments. As a result the vibration transmitted to the telescope is now no more than the background vibration which is caused, surprisingly, by the pounding of the sea on the island's shore, which makes the mountain ring like a tuning fork. Despite early misgivings vibration has not been a problem for the INT on La Palma.

Moving, upgrading and rehousing the INT cost the British taxpayer some £7.5 million, a figure that seems at first sight to justify Richard Woolley's earlier claim that relocating an existing telescope is almost as costly as building a new one. But in this case allowance must be made for the extra costs of the headquarters building. Even so there were dissenters who doubted whether it had been worth it, believing that the decision to move the telescope was another example of political expediency outweighing scientific good sense.

Regular observing with the reborn Isaac Newton Telescope began at the end of May 1984, when the first visiting astronomers arrived on the island to take their scheduled turns at the telescope. Hundreds more have made the pilgrimage to La Palma over the following 25 years, keeping the telescope fully occupied at every moment when conditions allowed. Even in the first two years, when the telescope was still being brought up to peak performance, a total of more than 1,600 observing hours was recorded by nearly 100 different observers, with more than 2,300 individual objects studied. (At this time almost all observations were spectroscopic, since the prime focus position, where direct observation was possible, had not yet been brought into service.)

Conditions for visiting observers were austere in the early days. The INT and JKT were operational before the residential accommodation was ready to provide day-time sleeping quarters for the astronomers and engineering staff. Temporary bedrooms were set up in containers tethered to the ground near the INT building. Conditions improved as the Spanish authorities fulfilled their part of the bargain: setting up the communal facilities and services that would serve the needs of all the national and international groups

The INT dome site atop the original ING headquarters building, which is protected from overheating by its corrugated solar screen.

who would use the new observatory. By 1985 the Residencia was nearing completion, a building where visiting astronomers could find food, accommodation, meeting rooms and recreational areas. It would come to act as a focal point and nerve-centre for an observatory that would eventually consist of many separate observing facilities scattered across the mountaintop. Flags at its entrance would represent the many countries involved – a total of fifteen by 2008.

In 1985 also, the tarred road up to the observatory finally reached completion. Its smoothly-graded 35-km (21-mile) ascent starts among the cacti and flowering shrubs of the island's lower slopes, before passing through needle-carpeted pine forest to emerge above the tree line onto the bare and rocky summit plain. With more than fifty hairpin bends, and rising a vertical distance of 2.4 km (1.5 miles), the route has tested the nerves and stomachs of a generation of astronomers. Newcomers are strongly advised to hire a local driver familiar with the road.

With the infrastructure in place a regular pattern for visiting astronomers soon emerged. As at Herstmonceux, advance planning begins months or even years ahead, with an application to the panel which shares out telescope time, explaining what observations would be made and making a scientific case for them. Successful applicants are then be allocated a certain number of nights, ranging from two or three to ten or more, and specific dates assigned. Astronomers visiting the Los Muchachos observatory usually fly in to one of the airports on the neighbouring island of Tenerife, and take the 30-minute hop by propeller plane to La Palma. The tortuous taxi-ride up the mountain delivers them to the Residencia to check in for meals and accommodation and pick up a torch and the keys of an observatory car – necessary since the INT is more than a mile away. A typical night's observing starts with dinner in the Residencia, served two hours before the sun goes down to everyone who will be busy at the observatory's many telescopes that night.

As darkness begins to fall – or sooner – INT users park outside the dome and make their way to the telescope control room on the third floor. For many years visiting astronomers had the services of a Night Assistant to operate the telescope for them. From 2003 however, to save money, the astronomers have had to do everything for themselves. A support astronomer is available to give a detailed briefing on the first afternoon of the run. Solo observers at the INT wear an alarm button for summoning help in an emergency.

Before observing can begin there is a checklist of tasks to run through. The ritual begins with the chore of topping up whichever instrument is currently in use with the telescope. Modern detectors perform best if kept at the temperature of -150°C and this is achieved by mounting them in containers cooled with liquid nitrogen. At the beginning and end of every night whoever is using the telescope must don protective headgear, gloves and apron, proceed to a suitable point in the dome to access the instrument, and top it up with liquid nitrogen from a large storage flask.

Back in the control room, a glance at the weather station monitor shows whether the conditions outside are within the limits for safe operation of the telescope. Fuente Nueva is a windy spot, but wind speeds up to a surprisingly high 80 kph (50 mph) – severe gale on the Beaufort scale – are acceptable, though the dome becomes a noisy place to work in under these conditions. Humidity has to be below 90 per cent, the value at which there is a risk of condensation inside the dome. To check for airborne dust it is only necessary to shine a torch into the darkness. If any dust can be seen in the beam the dome has to be closed. Special care must be taken in winter when there is a risk of the dome icing up so badly that it could not be opened or rotated, and observing becomes impossible.

Through the window from the Control Room the observer checks that the telescope is free to move, with no ladders or test equipment attached. If all is well, the dome shutters can be opened by pressing buttons on the control panel. Further button-pressing raises the petals which protect the primary mirror and switch on the fans to ventilate the dome. After that the dome lights can be turned off and the window blind closed. For the rest of the night's work everything is done by remote control, with the astronomer communicating with the telescope from inside the control room entirely by means of computer commands. There is no need to visit, or even look at, the telescope itself.

The INT control console in 1985. The astronomer on the right, Roy Wallis, is issuing instructions to the telescope via the computer keyboard.

Next the astronomer 'tells' the telescope, via the control computer, which mode to operate in, either at prime focus for obtaining images, or at Cassegrain focus for spectroscopy. Before the proper observing can begin a number of tests are run, including checking the output from the detector when no light is falling on it, so that this 'bias level' can be subtracted from later measurements. Observations of the twilight sky at this stage enable the system to subtract from the later observations spurious light coming from the sky rather than the object being studied.

To focus the telescope it is lined up on a patch of sky with a few stars and instructed to take a series of observations with the focus slightly altered between each one. The setting that gives the sharpest images is then selected.

Only when all this is completed can the astronomer begin the real business of the night, a series of observations – images or spectra – of the particular objects to be studied. A list of these with their sky co-ordinates can be typed into the computer's catalogue in advance. A simple computer instruction then causes the telescope to slew round to the required object and start to track it, a process known as acquisition. Simply typing an instruction such as 'run 60' or 'run 1200' starts an observation lasting 60 or 1,200 seconds (or whatever duration is required). As the exposure progresses, electric charges built up on the individual pixels of the CCD detector in response to the incoming light. At the end these are automatically read out as a string of digits to be transferred to a computer and permanently recorded on magnetic tape or DVD.

In an earlier era the astronomer had to keep an eye glued to a guiding telescope throughout the exposure, checking that the chosen object remained centred in the field of view, and moving the telescope to bring it back if it began to wander off. By the 1980s the process had been fully automated. On the new INT the autoguider, with its own CCD, can be locked on to a suitable star, close to the object actually being studied, and automatically ensures that that star, and hence the object of study in the main telescope, remains precisely centred throughout the observation. Movement of the dome is automatically synchronised with the motion of the telescope, ensuring that whichever direction the telescope is pointing it always has a clear view of the sky.

A typical night's work can involve hundreds of observations if the exposures are short (10-60 seconds) or much fewer if the objects are faint and require longer exposures (up to 30 minutes). The number of different objects observed may be few (sometimes just one or two) or many (50 or more), depending on the purpose of the study. Often an observation is repeated several times, with differing exposure times and through different colour filters. The CCD detectors only record the amount of light falling on them, not its colour. Using a filter to restrict the light reaching the detector to particular wavelength bands can yield more detailed information than would be seen in a white light image. Another use is in obtaining coloured images; if an object is imaged three times, through red, green and blue filters, the results can be combined to produce a true-colour image, showing how we would see the object if only our eyes were very much more sensitive.

Time is precious for observers awarded time on a large telescope, and the hours long. At La Palma an observer arriving at dusk and leaving at dawn is in the dome for 13 hours at midwinter, and 10 hours at midsummer. Sustenance is essential and the grab bag provided by the Residencia, with sandwiches, pizzas, drinks and other snacks, is welcome in the early hours. Equipment is provided in the dome for sandwich-toasting and coffee-making.

Stars leave trails as the Earth rotates during this time-exposure of the INT by night.

Paul Murdin, who has worked with the INT and many other large telescopes, has described how long exposure times afford plenty of time for thought: 'You can, to some extent, see the data as it comes in; it's displayed to you in rudimentary ways on the computer screens, and so you can develop your ideas as you go along. I find that this "communing process with nature" [is] the most productive scientific time. I feel directly connected from my eyes, through the monitors on the control desks, through the wires to the telescope, up towards the sky. I feel directly connected to this distant star that is sending this signal down towards me. I do not sit in the control room all the time thinking about this sort of thing. I wander about, and pace up and down and go outside and look at the sky. I look in the direction at which the telescope is pointing and I think of all those light particles that are travelling across space, coming down into my telescope and giving the data from which I am going to make my decisions.' Murdin is one of few people to have had opportunities to actually look through a large telescope, something only possible when for some technical reason serious scientific work has to be suspended. '... you are there with light from a galaxy or a planet or cluster of stars coming down into your eyeball, and seeing these things in the most amazing ways. What was something that looked like a little faint smudge when I was a schoolboy with a small telescope, when seen through a giant telescope, can be a dazzling galaxy, so bright you can practically not bear to look at it. You can see individual stars of different colours. Most amazingly, an almost three-dimensional image is produced for you by a big telescope.'[4]

The chance to look with the naked eye at a night sky that is crystal clear and totally uncontaminated by man-made light, is a privilege enjoyed by astronomers working on La Palma and at similar sites but denied to most other people in the industrialised world. Another observer at the INT has described stepping onto the roof outside the dome on a moonless night to be confronted by darkness more profound than anywhere else, except perhaps in an underground cave. As his eyes adapted to the dark the sky slowly filled with thousands of untwinkling points of light. The Milky Way – the edge-on view of our own galaxy – was particularly majestic, arching overhead with its lanes of obscuring dust silhouetted against the mass of more distant stars.[5] Another feature of the tropical sky, recalled by RGO astronomer Roger Wood, is the way the stars set; instead of fading slowly into the murk as they do at home, they march undimmed towards the horizon and are then snuffed out in an instant.

For observers at the INT, as daylight finally returns, it is time to put the telescope and dome to bed, bring the observing log up to date, top up the liquid nitrogen again and return to the Residencia to catch up on sleep, with the results of the night's work safely stored on tape cassettes or DVDs for study and analysis back home.

A copy of every item of data obtained by each of the telescopes of the Isaac Newton Group is also stored on computer at the Astronomical Data Centre at Cambridge University – nearly half a million observations in all. One year after an observation is made it becomes public property, accessible to anyone over the internet.

A distant galaxy (NGC6946) floats behind a sprinkling of nearby stars in this 1999 image from the INT's Wide Field Camera.

The born-again Isaac Newton Telescope was officially dedicated on 29th June 1985, as part of an elaborate inauguration ceremony for the new Observatorio del Roque de los Muchachos on La Palma, a venture in which seven European countries were by then involved. The event was attended by four crowned heads of state, from Denmark, The Netherlands, Spain and Sweden, together with the presidents of Ireland and West Germany and many other dignitaries. For Britain, the Queen did not attend (perhaps on the grounds that she had already inaugurated the INT once) but sent the Duke and Duchess of Gloucester in her place.

In contrast to the gloom and drizzle of Sussex at the first inauguration in December 1967, the occasion on La Palma took place under the crystal clear sky of the mountaintop. A day of ceremony and complex protocol began as the visiting dignitaries assembled by car and helicopter, discreetly watched over while on the island by bomb squad, anti-terrorist team and three thousand police drafted in for the occasion. The royal party moved from dome to dome to perform a series of inaugurations. In the Isaac Newton building some of the party ascended to the telescope floor by lift – the Spanish king and his son defying their security

Inauguration of the INT in 1985: RGO Director Alec Boksenberg (centre) briefs the Duke of Gloucester on what he should do. The man on the left is Prince Claus of The Netherlands.

team who had decreed that the monarch and his heir should not both travel in such a risky manner at the same time. The Duke of Gloucester unveiled a plaque and pressed a button to open the dome. As light flooded in he typed an instruction which lowered the telescope and caused it to open like a flower as the 'petals' protecting the main mirror lifted to reveal the reflecting surface below. The Duke then invited Queen Beatrix of the Netherlands to point the telescope to the north. As she activated the mechanism the assembled kings, queens, presidents, ministers and Nobel Prizewinners were amazed and delighted to witness a manoeuvre pre-scripted by Paul Murdin in which the dome turned in one direction and the telescope turned in the other, until the two were in perfect alignment. It was a *coup de théâtre* which, as one onlooker commented, was the part of the day that everyone was sure to remember. Disorientated by the contrary motion of dome and telescope, Queen Beatrix gasped and stepped smartly backwards, while King Juan Carlos of Spain lost his balance and nearly fell to the ground. After five more speeches in a specially constructed outdoor amphitheatre and the playing of seven national anthems, the party descended to sea level where the festivities concluded. La Palma had enjoyed its most exciting day since the Spaniards conquered the island in 1493.

It was left to the Chairman of the Science and Engineering Research Council, Sir John Kingman, to voice in an interview the huge feeling of relief many must have felt that the INT had finally been given a new lease of life and the whole embarrassing Herstmonceux episode in its life could be laid to rest. 'Now we have a site worthy of the Newton telescope', he said.[6] Herstmonceux's ugly duckling had finally become a swan.

Flags of the observatory's participating nations displayed at the entrance to the Residencia in 2008.

The universe from La Palma 10

THE FIRST SCIENTIFIC FINDING to come from the INT at its new site appeared in a paper published in November 1984, just eight months after the telescope saw first light. Its authors were Michael Penston of the RGO and Enrique Pérez of Sussex University and the RGO.[1] They had used the telescope to record the spectra of two galaxies of the Seyfert type – the bright-centred ones related to quasars – and had compared them with similar spectra taken of the same objects with the same telescope when it was at Herstmonceux. They found that in the intervening ten years, a mere eye-blink in astronomical terms, these galaxies had faded and their spectra had changed, showing that one variety of Seyfert galaxy might change into another. The re-sited INT had made its first contribution to science, a paper which would be cited by other scientists about 100 times in the years ahead.

More papers followed until by 1988 results from the INT were being published at an average rate of one a week – five times the rate in its Herstmonceux days. The INT on La Palma had become a small new tributary feeding into the river of worldwide astronomical progress. The main reason for the telescope's greatly increased scientific productivity was of course that it was a better telescope at a better site, but there was another factor too.

Astronomers in the 1980s were no longer restricted to viewing the universe simply by the visible light or radio waves it emitted. A range of new instruments and detectors, many of them satellite-borne, could pick up forms of radiation that had been invisible hitherto, mainly because they could not penetrate the atmosphere. Visible light is just a very small part of a much wider spectrum, each part of which has its own characteristic wavelength. Beyond the red end of the visible region lies the infrared (also known as

Colour images can be obtained by combining exposures made through three different colour filters. This 2004 image from the INT's Wide Field Camera shows the galaxy M74, some 30 to 40 million light-years distant. Clusters of young blue stars appear amongst pinkish gas clouds in the spiral arms.

radiant heat). Radiation at these wavelengths is mainly emitted by the cooler objects in the universe. Some of it can be detected by ground-based telescopes at high-altitude sites, such as in Hawaii, but much of the infrared band is only accessible from above the atmosphere. At still longer wavelengths, beyond the infrared, comes the broad radio region, explored by astronomers since the 1940s with ground-based radio telescopes, and later also from space.

At the other end of the spectrum, beyond the blue end of the visible region, comes first the ultraviolet region, followed by x-rays and finally gamma-rays. These radiations are mainly emitted by the hottest objects and the most violent processes in the universe. The atmosphere is opaque to all of them, so the universe can only be explored at these wavelengths from space. Satellites devoted to all these forms of 'invisible' astronomy were first launched in the 1960s and 70s. At the same time computer techniques became available to analyse the results sent back by satellites and often convert them into false-colour images which are the only ones human eyes can see. So much was learnt by studying the universe at all these wavelengths, that some referred to it as the New Astronomy. It was as though astronomers, who for generations had only been able to view the universe through a narrow slit, could now see it through a broad picture window.

All this had implications for the way ground-based optical telescopes such as the INT would be employed. In the past it was the norm to use a single technique, such as a particular spectroscope on a particular optical telescope, to study a variety of different objects. Now it was clear that many objects gave off a range of different forms of radiation, such as x-rays or radio waves in addition to visible light, and a new approach was needed. In future a typical research project might involve turning a variety of different instruments and detectors on to a particular object. Thus several telescopes, satellite-borne as well as ground-based, might be involved in the one piece of research, with each one doing what it could do best and sharing the credits in the published results. In the years ahead, instead of pursuing its own research projects, the INT would often be called on to play a supporting role in a much wider range of projects in which other telescopes were also involved.

Another major difference when comparing the new era with the old one is the extent to which computers and modern communications such as the internet are now involved. In many research papers more space is now given to explaining the statistics and mathematical manipulation used to process the observations once they have been obtained than to describing how they were procured in the first place. Instruments are pushed to their limits and great ingenuity is used to tease out results that are almost obscured by background noise and other effects. Readers of a paper will only have confidence that its findings are real if they can see exactly how the data have been treated.

Over the first quarter-century of its life on La Palma the INT would be involved with other telescopes in hundreds of projects, giving rise to more than a thousand scientific papers. It would observe thousands of different astronomical objects. Roughly half of these would be within our own galaxy, including some within the solar system. The other half would be in the deeper reaches of intergalactic space. In the review that follows some of the highlights of these many projects will be described, proceeding outwards from the fringes of the solar system to the depths of the universe.

At intervals in the twentieth century, astronomers speculated that there might be large numbers of small icy objects on the fringes of the solar system, remnants of the original solar system material

Some of the discovery frames from the INT on which Kuiper belt object 1993SC was first detected. It appears as a pale blue dot (magnitude 21.7) just above the centre of the upper frame. This had moved down and to the right (almost merging with a much more distant galaxy) in the lower frame taken a few hours later. The fact that the object was moved so fast indicates it must be in or near the solar system.

which never coalesced into a sizable planet. Though much too small to be dignified with the name planets, these objects would orbit the sun as all planets do, but at distances beyond the orbit of the most remote of the major planets, Neptune. In 1993 astronomers working with the INT joined the search for such objects, and on the nights of 16th and 17th September two were found. By taking pairs of exposures a few hours apart with the INT's Prime Focus CCD Camera it was possible to distinguish the extremely faint objects from background stars by the fact that they were moving. The new finds were designated 1993SB and 1993SC. They orbit the sun every 247 years, and through the action of gravity their motion is synchronised with that of Neptune so that they complete two orbits in precisely the time it takes Neptune to complete three orbits. Because Pluto behaves the same way, the objects are known as plutinos (little Plutos). Hundreds of plutinos are now known, but 1993SB and 1993SC were only the third and fourth to be discovered, two others having been spotted by American astronomers a few days earlier. 1993SC is the larger, with a diameter of around 200 miles, one sixth the size of Pluto. (Pluto's own status as a planet is currently a matter of debate).[2]

Astronomers from Belfast and Cambridge achieved an even more remarkable feat in 1997 when they used the INT with an updated CCD camera in the search for even more remote objects of this type. They spent seven nights obtaining exposures of up to four hours duration of an area of sky the size of the full moon. Computer processing of the combined results revealed two of the faintest objects ever seen in orbit round the sun. 1997UF25 and 1997UG25 lie beyond the orbit of Pluto and are probably less than 60 miles in diameter. 1997UF25 is the smaller of the two and because it is so far from the sun, so small, and probably dark in colour, it only appeared as a 25th magnitude object in the sky. (An object of this magnitude gives out so little light that were one to try to observe it from Earth with the naked eye, photons of light would enter one's eyes at a rate of less than one per hour.)

Thousands of these small objects are now known to lurk in outer regions of the solar system known as the Kuiper Belt and the Oort Cloud. They are significant because it is from here that comets come. Famously described as dirty snowballs, comets move in elongated orbits which periodically bring them close to the sun, whose heat causes them to grow their familiar tails of dust and gas. The INT has been used to study a number of comets during its time on La Palma, none more spectacular than comet Shoemaker-Levy 9 (SL9).

SL9 was unique among comets because it had been captured by the gravity of the planet Jupiter and at the time of its discovery was in orbit round that planet rather than round the sun. Even more astonishing was the prediction that in July 1994 the comet would actually collide with Jupiter. No collision between significant solar system objects had ever been recorded before; there was huge public interest, and astronomers around the world prepared the largest fleet of instruments ever mounted to study the event. The comet had already broken into 21 fragments, each designated by a letter of the alphabet, so there would be a succession of impacts with the planet. The ING telescopes were deputed to observe the impact of Fragment L, due on the evening of July 19th, with the INT recording spectra while its smaller neighbour, the JKT, obtained images.

The fireball created by the impact of Fragment L of Comet Shoemaker-Levy 9 with Jupiter is visible near the planet's south pole in this image from the JKT on La Palma. The INT obtained spectra of the event.

The event exceeded all expectation, *New Scientist* magazine calling it the 'celestial drama of the century'. Conditions were fine on La Palma at the crucial time, with resident RGO observers Nic Walton and Phil Rudd in the INT dome, and assistant Palmira Arenaz operating the telescope. Like a giant meteor, Fragment L vaporised explosively as it ploughed into Jupiter's atmosphere at 210,000 kph (130,000 mph), throwing out a huge plume of debris that spread to a height of about 3,200 km (2,000 miles). The impact itself was not visible from La Palma, but its site came into view a few minutes later as Jupiter turned. As arranged the INT's contribution to the worldwide observing effort was a series of spectra of the fireball, starting at the time of impact and continuing at intervals of a few minutes for the next hour and a half. They showed that atoms of sodium, magnesium, calcium and possibly iron were present in the fireball. These almost certainly originated in the comet fragment itself. The impact of Fragment L turned out to have been one of the most violent in the sequence. It left a dark scar the size of the Earth on the surface of Jupiter which remained visible from Earth in small telescopes for several weeks.[3]

The INT later took part in another large-scale international collaboration, also involving a comet and a collision. This was the *Deep Impact* mission in 2005 when an American spacecraft passed close to a comet, Tempel 1, and ejected an impactor with which the comet collided. The aim was to learn about the interior of the comet by creating a crater that would penetrate below the dirty surface into the pristine material below. Watching the event from Earth was an important part of the mission, with 73 telescopes involved at 35 observatories. Five La Palma telescopes took part, including the INT and WHT. The INT's important role was to observe the comet with the Prime Focus Camera during the periods when, due to the rotation of the Earth, it was not visible from the primary observing station in Hawaii. Observations began three nights before the impact and continued for three nights afterwards.

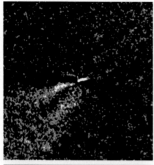

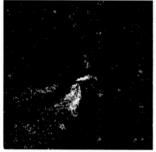

INT images were processed to show how jets of dust emanating from the dark nucleus of Comet Tempel 1 were affected by the collision with the impactor. The upper image shows the situation three days before impact, the lower one 16 hours after.

Conditions were excellent and hundreds of images were obtained during this period through a range of different filters. The moment of impact came in the early hours of July 4th, when the comet ran into the 300 kg (⅓ ton) impactor at 37,000 kph (23,000 mph). Tempel 1 was not visible from La Palma at that time, but when it returned to view 16 hours later the effect of the collision was immediately apparent. So much dust kicked up by the impact was now illuminated in sunlight that the comet's brightness had doubled. INT images showed how this dust cloud expanded and dissipated, and even revealed how the jets of dust and gas that comets emit when heated by the sun were affected by the impact. The comet was seen to return to its normal behaviour within a few days. The results of the whole mission were summarised in a paper which appeared in the journal *Science* a few months later. Two hundred and nine scientists from 86 institutions in 17 countries were listed as authors of this paper, including members of the INT team.[4]

Looking further afield, beyond the solar system and out among the billions of stars that make up our galaxy, we find the INT and other Canary Islands telescopes involved in the search for a new and hitherto unobserved type of object, christened a brown dwarf. Speculation since the 1970s had suggested that there might be large numbers of objects in the galaxy that are neither stars nor planets, but something between the two. Nicknamed 'failed stars' these would be objects, much less massive than normal stars, which formed in the same way as stars but because of their low mass never began to shine. Such light as they gave out would only be a dim red glow. If they existed in sufficient numbers brown dwarfs might provide a solution to one of astronomy's continuing mysteries, the nature of the missing mass, that preponderance of matter whose gravitational effect could be detected but which was otherwise completely invisible.

Searches for brown dwarfs had failed to produce definitive evidence until 1995, when a promising candidate was spotted with a telescope at the neighbouring Teide observatory on Tenerife. When further investigation with the William Herschel Telescope clinched the matter, the existence of brown dwarfs was unambiguously confirmed. Named Teide 1, the first example has a mass one twentieth that of the sun, but 50 times more than the planet Jupiter. In December 1995, the INT joined the search for more Brown Dwarfs. The Pleiades star cluster, 400 light-years away, was considered a good hunting-ground, and three nights imaging of a part of it enabled astronomers from Leicester University to identify ten faint deep-red objects which were likely candidates. Later work with the INT identified more possible brown dwarfs and today several hundred of these ghostly interlopers are known, but they are not thought to contribute significantly to the missing mass problem.[5]

In 1991 the INT returned to a problem it had first tackled at Herstmonceux, the positive identification of a black hole of the stellar type, formed when a massive star collapses at the end of its life. In the 1970s the target had been the double star system Cygnus X1 (see pages 74-75) but it had only been possible to conclude that it 'very probably' contained a black hole. Doubt remained because it was possible that the invisible object was sufficiently lightweight to be something other than a black hole. By the 1990s a new candidate had been identified, called V404 Cygni – the 404th variable star in the constellation of Cygnus, the Swan.

V404 had come to the attention of astronomers in 1938 when there was a spectacular, though short-lived, flare-up in its visible brightness, and again in 1979 when a Japanese satellite found a sudden huge increase in the x-rays coming from the same part of the sky – a definite clue that there might be a black hole at work. The RGO's Philip Charles, with British and Spanish colleagues, used the INT to investigate further. From spectra obtained over a single night in July 1990, after V404 had calmed down, they managed to show that there was indeed a faint star there which was orbiting round an invisible companion in the remarkably short time of once every 5.7 hours. Further spectra from the WHT enabled them to deduce that the invisible companion, though small, must be at least six times the mass of the sun (and at least twice the mass of the Cygnus X-1 black hole candidate). Basic physics shows that a stellar remnant that heavy must inevitably collapse to form a black hole, since no force exists that can stop this happening. So V404 provided, and at the time of writing still provides, the strongest known evidence that a black hole actually exists in our galaxy – a discovery for which the INT on La Palma shares the honours with its larger companion, the WHT.[6]

At the time the INT reopened on La Palma the only planets known to exist anywhere in the universe were the ones in our own solar system. Then in 1995, in one of the most exciting astronomical developments of the late twentieth century, two Swiss astronomers produced firm evidence that another star in our galaxy had its own orbiting planet. The planet could not be observed directly, but made its presence felt through the effect it had on its parent star. A heavy planet swinging round a lightweight star caused the star itself to move to and fro in a regular way, and this movement could be detected as a very slight change in wavelength of the star's spectral lines caused by the Doppler effect. In the following years more planets were found in orbit round other stars and it became clear that many – perhaps most – stars have their own planets. Many of the first 'exoplanets' to be discovered were unlike

A large galaxy comparatively close to our own remained unseen until 1994 when the INT's Prime Focus Camera produced this image. The galaxy is the faint S-shaped object in the centre. It appears dim because 99 per cent of its light is absorbed by dust in our own galaxy. The galaxy is named Dwingeloo-1 after the Dutch radio telescope which gave the first clue to its existence.

any in our own solar system: massive objects many times heavier than Jupiter, orbiting so close to the parent star that one year for these planets is only a few earth-days long. They became known as 'hot Jupiters'.

The INT joined the hunt for hot Jupiters in 1999, using a search technique called the transit method, which differs from the one described above. Calculations had shown that if the orbit of a hot Jupiter round its parent star happened to be lined up so that the planet passed precisely in front of the star as viewed from Earth, it would reveal its existence by blocking out a small, but measurable, fraction of the star's light – typically about one per cent – every time it passed in front. The search for hot Jupiters became a hunt for stars whose light regularly diminished very slightly for a period of a few hours and then returned to normal. A large number of stars would have to be checked, because even if a star did possess an orbiting hot Jupiter, the chance that it would happen to be lined up correctly for the transit effect to be visible from Earth was quite small. Astronomers from St Andrews University in Scotland, with colleagues from elsewhere, were allocated 30 nights of observing time with the INT's Wide Field Camera to search for hot Jupiters. By focussing on clusters where many stars are in the field of view simultaneously, they were able to monitor 120,000 different stars. They expected to find a small number of hot Jupiters in their sample, and a number of possible candidates were indeed found. Unfortunately none of them stood up to more detailed scrutiny. Hot Jupiters, it seemed, were not as common as expected.[7]

The story continues more happily however. Astronomers from six British UK universities, led by Queen's University, Belfast and including St Andrews, joined forces with colleagues from the Isaac Newton Group and the Astronomical Institute of the Canary Islands, to create the WASP Consortium, where WASP stands for Wide Angle Search for Planets. They constructed two special-purpose robotic instruments each made up of eight paparazzi-style cameras, together capable of monitoring the light from a million stars each month looking for the telltale signature of transiting planets. One of these instruments was installed alongside the ING on La Palma. The project's members have been well-rewarded for their efforts: in the first three years of operation the two WASP instruments discovered 15 hot Jupiter planets orbiting stars up to 1,000 light-years from Earth. The INT played a supporting role, helping to supply some of the spectra that confirmed the existence of the new planets.[8]

While some astronomers were looking for specific types of object, others were using the INT for survey work – the astronomical equivalent of mapping a continent, rather than seeking a few rare beasts that roam there. The RGO had a long history of such surveys. Its very purpose, when founded in 1675, was that the first Astronomer Royal should prepare a better map of the sky than any then available. Two centuries later a special telescope was purchased (now at Herstmonceux) to enable the observatory to take part in a global effort to photograph and map the entire night sky. A hundred years later still, the marriage of digital detectors with the massive data-handling power of computers gave new impetus to survey work, and a new role for the INT. What had been a large telescope in the 1960s was now regarded as a small one. One of the INT's neighbours at the Los Muchachos observatory, GranTeCan, would have 16 times as much light-gathering power, and would be by no means the only one of this size. For many 21st-century projects the INT could not compete with these giants. But for time-consuming surveys, where a large area of sky is to be covered bit by bit, the INT with its Wide Field Camera was well placed to participate. Survey work is also an area where ground-based telescopes can compete favourably with the Hubble Space Telescope, which is not equipped for use in that way.

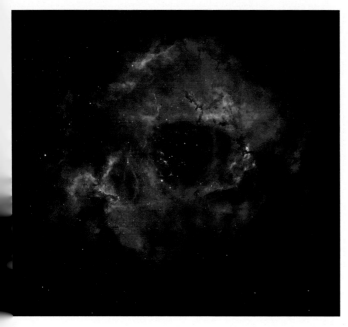

Red-filtered INT images obtained for the IPHAS project were stitched together to produce this spectacular picture of a glowing cloud of hydrogen gas known as the Rosette nebula (NGC2237). The gas is heated from within by new young stars, not visible here. The area covered is about 20 times that of the full moon.

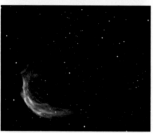

More WFC images, red-filtered to pick out the light from glowing hydrogen atoms. These are Planetary Nebulae, expanding shells of gas blown out by dying stars. From the top: NGC6888, Sharpless 2-188, Sharpless 2-200.

One of these survey was initiated in the early years of the new millennium when 50 scientists from five countries joined forces for a major UK-led project. The aim was to use the INT to obtain detailed images of the entire swathe of the northern sky we know as the Milky Way. Objects as faint as 20th magnitude would be included, but the images would not show the Milky Way as we normally see it. For the new survey the INT would view the sky through deep red filters selecting only the light that comes from hydrogen atoms that have lost their attendant electron, the so-called Hydrogen-alpha spectrum line. This would bring into view diffuse clouds of hydrogen in the galaxy, and also identify some rare types of star, the very old and the very young ones, about which there was still much to be learnt. More than this, the reams of data generated by the survey would be made available to everyone. Astronomers would mine this immense resource for years ahead, extracting information relevant to their own research interests.

The survey was officially called IPHAS, the INT Photometric Hydrogen Alpha Survey (photometric because the brightness as well as the position of every object would be measured). It was a huge venture into production-line astronomy. Because a large area of sky was involved, and the telescope could only view a small patch at a time, the relevant area had to be divided into a mosaic of 7635 small squares. Each of these required six exposures (two each with three different filters), taking a total of 10 minutes observing time. Work started in 2003 and was shared amongst a team of observers who between them spent 200 nights at the telescope in the first two years alone. Preliminary results, announced in 2007, gave details of more than 200 million separate objects revealed in the survey, and produced dramatic red images of objects never seen in so much detail before. IPHAS was turning up unexpected results, and even before the observational stage was complete more than 40 research papers had been published based on its findings. 'Data mining' from an office desk might lack the glamour of first-hand work with big telescopes in exotic locations, but it is a productive – and cost-effective – way to do research.[9]

Another survey project to which the INT contributed produced the Millennium Galaxy Catalogue, a high resolution 'photo album' of 10,000 galaxies lying in a narrow band along the equator of the sky – a project in which UK astronomers collaborated with colleagues in Germany and Australia. One remarkable finding from this, announced in 2008, is that the universe is actually shining twice as brightly as previously thought. This is because half the light emitted by each galaxy is absorbed by dust grains within the galaxy itself.[10]

As already mentioned, the INT has spent roughly half its time looking out beyond our own galaxy to deeper regions inhabited by galaxies and quasars. 'Quasarology' had been an exciting new field of research for the INT at Herstmonceux, and remained so at its new site. There was no longer much doubt about what quasars actually are, but being hugely bright they were valuable tools for probing conditions at distances where we see the universe as it was billions of years ago. The more distant the quasar, the closer it takes us to the Big Bang itself. As a result astronomers vied to discover more and more distant examples, with the INT playing an important part in the hunt. The aim was not to achieve an entry in the *Guinness Book of Records*, however, but to try to find how soon after the birth of the universe galaxies and quasars began to form.

A candidate quasar identified as a faint red dot on an image could be confirmed using a spectrograph to measure its redshift. In 1989 two Cambridge astronomers, Richard McMahon and Michael Irwin, used the INT to obtain spectra which led to the discovery of quasars so remote that their light is stretched – redshifted – by a factor of five, indicating that in the time the quasar's light has taken to reach the Earth, the universe has expanded by the same factor. That in turn implies that light from the quasar has taken about 11 billion years to arrive and started its journey when the universe was little more than a tenth its present age. Quasars with such high redshifts seem to be extremely few and far between. Only four were known at that time, and three of them had been discovered with the INT. The Cambridge researchers pushed the limit even further when they identified a number of suspiciously red-looking objects in the data from another of the INT's survey projects. Follow-up spectra from the WHT confirmed that one of these was a quasar redshifted by a factor of 6.2, the fourth highest known at that time.[11]

Quasar research threw up some interesting surprises, as Irwin and his colleagues discovered in 1998. While studying something else with the INT, they came upon an object which was undoubtedly a far-distant quasar but also seemed to shine with extraordinary brilliance. This quasar, it seemed, was the brightest single object in the universe by a substantial margin. But appearances were deceptive. The discovery team surmised that the brightness might be a mirage. An unseen object somewhere in the line of sight between the Earth and the quasar might be acting as a gravitational lens, converging the quasar's light in our direction and making it look much brighter than it really is. Follow-up work with the Hubble Space Telescope confirmed that this is in fact the case. The quasar, APM 08279+5255, is not after all the brightest object in the universe, but it may still hold the record for the most distant object that can be seen with the sort of telescope possessed by some amateur astronomers.[12]

Observation of another remote object enabled the INT to

The light that gave rise to the tiny red dot at the centre of this INT image travelled across the universe for about 12 billion years before entering the telescope in 1995. The dot is the quasar GB1428+4217, the third most distant discovered by that time. Its high redshift means that light which was blue when it left the quasar is deep red when it reaches the Earth.

play a small part in unravelling one of the biggest mysteries of late-twentieth century astronomy, finding the origin of short-lived but violent bursts of high-energy radiation that assault our planet at random roughly once a day. Known as gamma-ray bursts, these events had first come to light in the 1960s when they were picked up by military satellites designed for the quite different purpose of watching for illicit testing of nuclear weapons. Only in 1973 was the existence of these bursts made public, and for the next quarter-century astronomers could only speculate on what sort of cataclysmic process occurring somewhere in the universe might give rise to such violent events. Some thought the source might be local, somewhere within our own galaxy or even at the edge of the solar system; others thought the bursts were cosmic in origin, perhaps originating billions of light-years away.

The breakthrough came on 28th February 1997. At 2.58 GMT that morning an Italian satellite, *BeppoSAX*, able to detect gamma rays which cannot penetrate to ground level, picked up an 80-second burst of gamma rays coming from roughly the direction of the constellation Orion. *BeppoSAX* also carried an x-ray telescope and when the Italian and Dutch scientists running the project turned this towards the region where the gamma-rays seemed to originate, they found a strong new source of x-rays where none had been before, indicating that the gamma and x-rays probably came from the same source. They were able to pinpoint the position of this source so precisely that for the first time optical astronomers could be told where to point their telescopes. By good fortune a leading Dutch expert on gamma ray bursts, Jan van Paradijs, had booked some observing time on the William Herschel Telescope that very evening. Instructions were phoned through to La Palma where, by further good fortune, the right bit of sky would be visible that night, and the weather was clear. Twenty-one hours after the burst occurred, the WHT was turned to the relevant point in the sky. The resulting image showed what everyone had been waiting for, a faint patch of light, which, crucially, had become much fainter when the INT took another look at it eight days later – just as one would expect if this was indeed the optical afterglow of the event that produced the original gamma ray burst.

At last astronomers had their 'smoking gun', the optical counterpart of a gamma ray burst. Soon other telescopes found evidence of a distant galaxy associated with the faint and fading optical object, confirming at last that gamma ray bursts originate in remote parts of the universe. When news of this discovery came out, astronomers, in the words of *New Scientist*, 'went wild'. The discovery was hailed as one of the top five scientific breakthroughs of the year by *Science* magazine.[13]

Today most gamma ray bursts are thought to arise when a heavyweight star – 20 to 30 times more massive than the sun –

somewhere in a distant galaxy reaches the end of its life. In an explosion hundreds of times more violent than a normal supernova, the star's core collapses to become a black hole, and a complex process converts the energy released into two jets of gamma rays heading in opposite directions. Only if one of these jets happens to be directed towards our own galaxy do we detect the gamma ray burst, millions or even billions of years after the explosion actually occurred. We are not endangered by these events however; even though gamma rays are more energetic than x-rays they do not penetrate the earth's atmosphere to reach the ground.

Ever since astronomers began to use photography they had known that by increasing the length of an exposure they could reveal fainter and fainter objects in the sky. The advent of electronic detectors brought a new possibility; by combining images of the same area of sky obtained in a number of separate exposures it was now possible to produce the equivalent of one extremely long exposure.

The results of a remarkable application of this technique were reported by Nigel Metcalfe and colleagues from the University of Durham in 1995. On a number of moonless nights over a three-year period they took 59 exposures with the INT's Prime Focus Camera, most of them lasting 25 or 30 minutes. All were aimed at exactly the same patch of sky. They then stacked these images to produce the equivalent of a single exposure lasting 26 hours, from which the effects of background light had been subtracted. The result was that extremely faint objects invisible in the individual exposures became visible in the combined one. In a small area of sky where nothing at all can be detected with the naked eye, the 26-hour exposure revealed the presence of more than 4000 extremely faint and remote galaxies.

The purpose of the exercise was not simply to count the galaxies. The Durham team also measured the apparent brightness of each galaxy. These galaxies are at differing distances from Earth and therefore appear at a range of different brightnesses. The faintest are so remote that we see them as they were when the universe was young, which is why deep field images of this sort are an important way of exploring the early evolution and large-scale structure of the universe. The INT's deep field image was followed by similar ones from other telescopes, including the Hubble Space Telescope. The Durham team went on to combine their original INT image with 30-hours exposure of the same piece of sky from the larger William Herschel Telescope. Since most of the data came from the WHT, the resulting composite image is known as the William Herschel Deep Field.[14]

For the layperson, deep field images of this sort come as a revelation. They help us appreciate just how truly vast the universe

The INT contributed 26 hours of observing time to this extraordinary image, a joint venture with the WHT. It shows a tiny patch of sky hugely magnified, and with extremely faint objects visible. The smaller objects are all distant galaxies – several thousand in all. The faint blue ones are so remote that we see them as they were much earlier in the history of the universe.

is. The area of sky studied in the INT deep field experiment was tiny – roughly one tenth the size of the patch of sky blocked out by a single grain of rice held at arm's length. Yet it is home to several thousand galaxies, each much the same as our own Milky Way with its hundred billion stars. And there was nothing very special about the particular region of the constellation Pisces studied in the deep field project. Had the telescope been pointed somewhere else in the sky a similar image with thousands of other galaxies would have been the result. Wherever one points a powerful telescope in the sky (apart from regions where dust and gas in our own galaxy block the view) its line of sight eventually ends on thousands of tiny galaxies. Astronomers call them 'the wallpaper'. If the entire sky could be imaged with the INT in the way that the Durham astronomers imaged one small patch, more than five billion galaxies would come to view – but that would still only be a small fraction of all the galaxies believed to exist in the universe.

As the universe expands these galaxies spread further and further apart. At the same time they all exert gravity on each other, so astronomers expected that the expansion of the universe must slow down as time went on. But they did not have the data to say whether this deceleration would eventually be enough to bring the universe to a standstill, and perhaps even cause it to collapse back down to a Big Crunch. In the 1990s an ambitious project set out to answer this question by actually measuring the expected change in the universe's rate of expansion. The yardstick used to make this measurement would be supernovae, and one of the telescopes used to observe them would be the INT.

Much had been learnt about supernovae in the years since the INT had kept watch on SN1974g in the skies above Herstmonceux. Better ways had been found to classify the different types, and in particular to identify the ones, now known as Type 1a supernovae, which could be used as 'standard candles' because wherever they occur in the universe they always reach the same maximum brightness. By good fortune, the brightest supernova of the twentieth century visible from the northern hemisphere erupted in March 1993. All three ING telescopes were quickly brought into play to study it, with the INT the first in the world to obtain a spectrum, just one day after its discovery. A major observing programme followed on La Palma, using telescope time cadged from scheduled observers, with the results made available online to astronomers worldwide.[15] Remarkably, three more exceptional supernovae appeared the following year, prompting one astronomer to observe that supernovae appeared to obey 'London bus' statistics – you wait ages for one and then four come along at once.

But these unscheduled appearances were all in nearby galaxies, and their randomness was disruptive in a world where telescope time was fully allocated many months in advance. Rather than waiting for supernovae to turn up, a young astronomer from California, Saul

The 4.2-metre William Herschel Telescope joined the INT on La Palma in 1987. It is seen here under construction at the Grubb Parsons works. Designed by RGO staff, it has proved an outstandingly successful instrument.

Perlmutter, was devising a way to search for them, aiming to replace 'supernovae-by-chance' with 'supernovae-on-demand'. His method was a simple one in principle. In any one galaxy just one or two Type 1a supernovae occur every thousand years, so huge numbers of galaxies would have to be canvassed. Wide-field images would be obtained of an area of sky rich in distant galaxies, so that tens of thousands of galaxies could be acquired in just one or two moonless nights at a single telescope. Three weeks later the same images would be repeated at the same telescope. A frenzy of computer processing and analysis would then follow in which the new and old images of each galaxy would be compared, with a reasonable certainty that in such a large sample a few fresh supernovae would have appeared in the meantime.

The beauty of the method was that the date when a new batch of supernovae might be harvested was predictable months in advance, so that telescope time could be booked for the essential follow-up study each new supernova would require. Type 1a supernovae take a few days to reach their peak brightness, and the best data are obtained at this early stage. Provided the mass of computer work could be completed in just a day or two, Perlmutter's technique would allow the follow-up observations to begin before the supernova reached its peak, and before the waxing moon returned to interfere with the observations.

The goal was to find about 30 new Type 1a supernovae, more remote than any seen before. For each, just two measurements would be needed. Its measured brightness would allow a calculation of how far its light had travelled (since all Type 1a supernovae have the same, known, *actual* brightness) and hence how long the journey must have taken. Its measured redshift would indicate how much the universe had expanded while the light was on its way. From the two figures – journey time and redshift – the average rate of expansion of the universe during the time the light was travelling could be worked out. Finally, repeating the measurements for supernovae at different distances would reveal whether the rate of expansion was actually decreasing over time as expected.

The logic was impeccable, but the practical difficulties formidable. To test his method, Perlmutter needed to book telescope time months ahead for the follow-up observations on objects which might or might not have been discovered when the time came. Telescope time is scarce, and operators were unwilling to commit it to such a speculative venture. Eventually however he was given time on the INT to prove the method.

Work began on La Palma on 24th March 1992 when the first of 54 images was taken with the INT's Prime Focus Camera. As planned, these were repeated the following month. The data were sent to California for processing and the results returned two days later. With 10,000 galaxies canvassed the experiment had a good chance of success, and so it proved. Just one new supernova was found, but one was enough to show the method had potential. The new find was designated SN1992bi, and its progress was followed for several more weeks with the INT. By August the supernova had faded but the galaxy of which it was part remained visible. When the WHT obtained spectra from this galaxy it was found to have a redshift that placed it at a distance of about 5 billion light-years. SN1992bi was the most remote supernova yet discovered. The actual explosion had happened at about the time when the solar system was formed.[16]

Perlmutter's Supernova Cosmology Project (SCP), as it was now known, was gaining momentum. The discovery team for the first supernova numbered 23 people from 10 institutions. Four of them were from the RGO. In the following two years the team netted seven more of these distant supernovae, five of them discovered by the INT.[17] By now other observatories were happy to provide observing time for a project with exciting prospects and larger telescopes with greater penetrating power took over some of the work, though the INT continued to help with the follow-ups.

By January 1998 the SCP had data from 40 supernovae, including one half the universe away, and Perlmutter was ready to reveal what they told us about the universe. To the astonishment of almost everyone, it appeared we were in a universe whose expansion was not slowing down at all; in fact it was speeding up. If this result was right, it would overturn the established wisdom of half a century, with profound implications for fundamental physics as well as cosmology. Fortunately a rival team led by an Australian astronomer had been running a parallel operation using a different set of supernovae, and their results supported what the SCP had found.

A measure of the impact of the Supernova Cosmology Project can be found in the fact that the definitive paper describing its result has since been cited by other authors nearly 4000 times.[18] Ten years later the SCP results still stand, despite concerted efforts to find flaws in the research. The idea of an accelerating universe is something cosmologists are learning to live with. The mysterious anti-gravity that must be pushing the universe apart has been given a name, dark energy, but there is little accord about what it is. There is no doubt, however, that a research project which took off when the INT discovered its first new supernova in 1992 has gone on to cause a scientific earthquake.

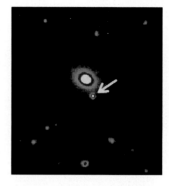

Type 1a supernova in a distant galaxy. In this 1998 false-colour image from the INT's Wide Field Camera, the larger object is an unnamed galaxy more than a billion light-years away. The arrow shows where a star in the outer part of the galaxy is undergoing a supernova eruption.

Epilogue

WHILE THE INT and its sister telescopes were building themselves a fine reputation under the clear skies of the Canary islands, the news from Sussex was bad and getting worse. Administrative upheavals and financial crises originating at home would repeatedly buffet the La Palma operation during its first quarter-century of operation.

In a sense La Palma's success was Herstmonceux's downfall. Staff at the RGO had responded well to their new role as providers of observing facilities for university astronomers, and made an excellent job of setting up and equipping the La Palma observatory. But with the INT gone, the Sussex site had lost much of its *raison d'être*. Astronomy had moved on and the RGO, with its three hundred years of history, was getting left behind. Some of its remaining services and activities had a distinctly dated feel to them. It was only a matter of time before the question would be raised of whether one really needed a mediaeval castle and 358 acres of Sussex countryside in order to service an observatory 2000 miles away and provide its other services. The people who eventually asked that question were the members of a government cost-cutting unit led by Sir Derek Rayner. Even before the INT was in operation on La Palma they produced a review proposing that the Herstmonceux Castle estate should be sold, and that the RGO might merge with its Scottish counterpart, the Royal Observatory, Edinburgh.

In the event the merger did not go ahead, but the sale of the castle did. To save money and in the teeth of fierce opposition both from the staff and members of the wider astronomical community, the observatory was compelled to move in 1990 to a newly-built office building in Cambridge. Whether the closure of

Herstmonceux can be blamed directly on the removal of the INT is debatable. It may be that the RGO was already living on borrowed time. But if the INT had still been there, selling Herstmonceux would have been a less attractive option and a messier business. As it was, the solution of one problem, what to do about the INT, had exposed a worse one, what to do about the RGO.

The move to Cambridge turned out to be merely a stay of execution. Just eight years later the unthinkable happened. Faced with a deep cut in government funding, the research council responsible for astronomy decided that it could no longer afford to run two astronomical research establishments in the UK, at Cambridge and Edinburgh. It was the Cambridge one that had to go. So on 30th October 1998, after 323 years of service to the nation, the Royal Greenwich Observatory closed its doors for ever. Its remaining functions were either discontinued or transferred elsewhere. Some staff were found work with other organisations, including a newly-established Astronomy Technology Centre in Edinburgh, and others lost their jobs.

Herstmonceux castle and estate remained in limbo for some years after the departure of the observatory, but eventually came back to life after they were bought by a benefactor for use as an International Study Centre by a Canadian university.[1] Today students inhabit the Castle and other buildings, while the Equatorial Group of telescopes hums with activity as a flourishing Science Centre.[2] Only the INT dome remains lifeless, attempts to reinvigorate it as an arts arena having met with no success. For its

The abandoned INT building at Herstmonceux in 2007.
a – exterior of the dome;
b – closure notice;
c – the telescope control desk;
d – the public viewing gallery.

critics it may stand as a latter-day example of a folly, one of those pointless structures whose existence merely betrays the foolishness of its builder. But for others it appears to have acquired a mystical status akin to that of Stonehenge, serving as a focus for outdoor music-making and new age activities associated as much with astrology as astronomy. Perhaps, if this unlikely object survives as a prominent feature in the Sussex landscape, it will inspire in future generations the same mixture of awe and fascination as that enigmatic circle of stones on the Wiltshire plain.

Above: the original 98-inch Pyrex mirror is moved into place for permanent redisplay at the Observatory Science Centre at Herstmonceux.

Below: the mirror on display.

The demise of the RGO in October 1998 inevitably had implications for La Palma. Funding cuts had already led to belt-tightening there, with the result that visiting astronomers at the INT no longer enjoyed the support of a telescope operator and would be restricted in the choice of instruments and detectors available for the telescope. RGO staff had played a key part in most aspects of the design, construction and first years of operation of the telescopes and instruments on La Palma. With the closure of the home observatory, much more work on the telescopes and their instruments would have to be done on the island by the ING's own staff. The new millennium saw a further round of cost-cutting, including in 2003 the closure of the smallest of the ING's instruments, the Jacobus Kapteyn Telescope, and a concentration of resources on upgrading the William Herschel Telescope. Spain took on a greater share of the Group's running costs in return for an increased fraction of the observing time. Yet another funding crisis in British science in 2007-8 brought the threat that Britain's contribution might have to be halved. There was even a possibility that the Isaac Newton Group might one day have to run with no support at all from Isaac Newton's homeland.

Through all this the ING, now leaner and more cost-efficient, continued to serve the astronomical community extremely well, with no evidence of a shortage of tasks for its telescopes to do, or astronomers wanting to use them. Citation analysis, of the type done earlier by Irvine and Martin, showed how well the La Palma telescopes had performed in the 1990s in terms of their research output, compared to others of similar size. A review of the ING by independent experts in 2001 also gave a very positive assessment. At a time when the world's largest telescopes had 8- or even 10-metre apertures, there were still excellent prospects for telescopes in the 2- to 4-metre class to carry out 'frontline science that is well matched to their medium aperture and large field'. The WHT ranked in 'the top two 4-metre class telescopes in the world', while the INT was 'well ranked among the world's 2-metre class telescopes, in terms of impact and productivity'.[3]

The La Palma site, first brought to attention in the 1970s by RGO astronomers looking to re-site the INT, has grown into one of the world's pre-eminent observing sites, matched only by those in Hawaii, Chile and the south-west United States. Walking among the gleaming white domes of the Los Muchachos observatory has been likened to touring a futuristic martian outpost. Its success owes much to the extraordinary zeal of one Spanish astronomer, Francisco Sánchez, founder and director general of the Canaries Institute of Astronomy (IAC) which runs the Teide Observatory on Tenerife along with the one on La Palma. More than 60 institutions in 19 countries now have shares in telescopes at the two observatories. The resulting renaissance in Spanish astronomy has been spectacular. When Sánchez started work in the 1960s Spain had just four professional astronomers. Now there are more than 400, of whom 150 are permanent research staff.

One of La Palma's greatest assets is the lack of light pollution, and the Spanish authorities have acted to ensure it stays that way. The Canary Sky Law which came into force in 1992 controls the way outdoor lighting is used on the island. Lamps must never shine upwards, and certain types must be extinguished at midnight. To test the success of these measures every street lamp on the island was switched off for an hour on the occasion of the observatory's tenth birthday in 1995. When they came back on it was possible to determine just how small the contribution is that they inevitably make to sky brightness at the observatory, firm evidence that the La Palma night sky is quite as dark as at other first-rank observing sites.

The history of the Isaac Newton Telescope is a two-act drama which hopefully still has some way to run. The 'damned telescope' of Herstmonceux was born of hope in an age of austerity, suffered years of indecision, delay and controversy, and was finally brought down by the realities of the English climate. Judged by the standards of its time, however, it is something in which its creators can take some pride. Through their efforts the telescope to commemorate Britain's greatest scientist did eventually get built and at the time of completion was the fifth largest in the world. It was not perfect, but it worked pretty well. Despite the weather, astronomers did use it at Herstmonceux and their observations gave rise to about 100 papers in scientific journals. It was a spectacular piece of cutting-edge technology which engendered popular interest in astronomy and attracted many visitors to Herstmonceux, boosting the prestige of the observatory and of science generally. Building it was valuable

Three views of galaxy M51 show the effects of improving technology:
a – drawing by William Parsons as seen through his 'Leviathan' telescope, 1845;
b – photograph from the INT at Herstmonceux, 1970;
c – digital image from the INT on La Palma, 2000.

experience for scientists and engineers at the RGO who would go on to set up larger telescopes on La Palma and elsewhere. It was a salutary object lesson for scientists and science administrators who would go on to run other 'big science' projects more successfully. In the words of Francis Graham Smith, the INT at Herstmonceux 'had an enormous influence on British astronomy, because for the first time there was a large instrument available to people from British universities, and it started the pattern of British universities using what we now call national facilities'.[4]

From just 15 posts for professional astronomers in the UK in 1945, there are now about 350. From an era when there was next to no postgraduate training there are now more than 300 postgraduate astronomy students at more than 20 British universities. Between the two is a solid cadre of postdoctoral fellows; that half of them are drawn from overseas is evidence of Britain's standing in astronomy, second only to that of the USA. So the hoped-for resurgence in British observational astronomy really did take place, and the Isaac Newton Telescope undoubtedly played a part in it.

That the Herstmonceux telescope was transformed into one worthy of a world-class site 'above the grosser clouds' and despite everything is still busy there twenty-five years later, is a tribute to the staff of the RGO and the ING who adapted it and continue to sustain it. In the words of one of them, Javier Méndez Alvarez, 'the INT continues to perform very well. It's an outstandingly productive 2-metre class telescope, producing between 60 and 80 refereed papers in the main astronomical journals per year. It has superb optics and instrumentation; it's efficiently operated and it's located in a fantastic observing site.'[5]

More than sixty years have passed since Harry Plaskett made the speech that initiated the INT project. In that time optical astronomy has evolved and blossomed, in Britain and abroad, and grown into a truly international science. New opportunities for telescopes like the INT, small instruments though they are by modern standards, continue to appear. Developments in electronics and computing have transformed their capabilities. And in sixty years the universe has revealed some spectacular secrets – and posed some intriguing new questions.

Yet at heart the INT is what it always was, simply a curved mirror facing out towards the night sky, catching and focussing whatever light comes in. If Isaac Newton could visit La Palma today he would be amazed to see the instrument that bears his name, but he would have no difficulty understanding what it does. Three and a half centuries ago he made its prototype himself.

Sources

Sources prefixed RGO are documents in the archives of the Royal Greenwich Observatory held in Cambridge University Library. Quotations from these appear by permission of the Science and Technology Facilities Council and the Syndics of Cambridge University Library.

Sources prefixed ADS are papers whose full bibliographic details and complete text can be found by going to the website *www.adsabs.harvard.edu* and typing the 19-character code (including all the dots) into the search box.

Introduction (page 9)

1 Plaskett, H.H., quoted in 'The Isaac Newton Observatory', Sadler, D. H., *The Observatory*, vol. 66, pp. 380-3 (1946)
2 Lyttleton, R.A., letter to *The Times*, 24 Feb 1973, p. 13
3 Newton, I,. 'Opticks', Dover Publications edition (1952), p. III

Chapter 1 (pages 13-20)

1 RGO 9/129: Report of the Committee on Post-War Needs in Astronomy
2 Ibid.
3 ADS 1946MNRAS.106...80P
4 ADS 1947MNRAS.107...II.
5 RGO 9/129: Spencer Jones, H., to the Hydrographer of the Navy, letter, 17 July 1947
6 ADS 1946Obs....66..308.
7 *The Observatory*, vol 66, p. 380-3 (1946).
8 Bates, W., letter to *The Times*, 31 Jan 1973, p. 15

Chapter 2 (pages 21-29)

1 ADS 1946Obs....66..308

Chapter 3 (pages 30-40)

1 McCauley, G.V. 'Corning Glass Works and Astronomical Telescopes', typescript held in the archives of Corning Incorporated, N.Y., U.S.A. (1965)
2 www.mcgregorfund.org
3 RGO 9/129: Uttley, A.M., to H. Spencer Jones, letter, 24 May 1948
4 RGO 9/129: Goldberg, L., to A. M. Uttley, letter, 14 June 1948
5 RGO 9/129: Hulbert, H., to H. Spencer Jones, letter, 6 Sept 1948
6 RGO 37/51: Linfoot, E.H., Report on his examination of the INT disc, 30 Dec 1950

Chapter 4 (pages 41-53)

1 Statement accompanying minutes of meeting of RGO Board of Visitors, 11 June 1960, Royal Society archives 98 HF 177.12
2 ADS 1987Obs....107...99S
3 RGO 10/641: INT Board of Management: minutes of 13th meeting, 5 March 1956
4 *The Times*, 17 Jan. 1949, p. 5
5 RGO 10/641: INT Board of Management: minutes of 17th meeting, 25 April 1962

6 Papers relevant to this incident are in the National Archives, file CAB 124/3035
7 Minutes of meeting of RGO Board of Visitors,, 11 June 1960, Royal Society archives 98 HF 177.II
8 ADS 1964Obs....84..216F
9 *Eastbourne Gazette*, December 1967
10 *Daily Express*, 1 December 1967. The astronomer was Margaret Penston.
11 ADS 1982JHA....13....1S
12 *The Times*, 29 July 1968; p. 23

Chapter 5 (pages 54-67)

1 McCrea, W.H., 'The Royal Greenwich Observatory', HMSO (1975), p. 66
2 A number of descriptive articles about the INT and its dome appeared around the time of its inauguration, principally: ADS 1962QJRAS...3..249W ; ADS 1964Obs....84..169. ; *Nature*, vol. 216, p.855-6 (1967); *Yearbook of Astronomy* 1967, pp. 102-9; *Sky and Telescope*, Dec 1967, pp. 356-61; *The Engineer*, 15 Dec 1967, p. 791-2
3 Reported in *The Daily Mirror* and *The Times*, 1 Dec 1967
4 ADS 1977QJRAS..18..351H
5 ADS 1969Obs....89...85.

Chapter 6 (pages 68-81)

1 *The Times*, 8 Sept 1967 p. 5; *Royal Greenwich Observatory Bulletin* No. 159, p. 83-109 (1970).
2 *Nature*, vol 221, p. 1229 (1969)
3 ADS 1975MNRAS.172..289B
4 *Nature*, vol 223, p. 690 (1969)
5 ADS 1976MNRAS.174...47D
6 *Nature*, vol 274, p. 37 (1978).
7 *Nature*, vol 233, p. 110 (1971).
8 *Nature*, vol 235, p. 37 (1972).
9 ADS 1976MNRAS.175..595P
10 ADS 1998ApJ...509...80S

Chapter 7 (pages 82-93)

1 ADS 1994ARA&A..32....1B
2 *Nature*, vol 222, p. 845 (1969)
3 *Nature*, vol 222, p. 1215 (1969)
4 ADS 1991QJRAS..32....1L
5 Mitton, S., 'Fred Hoyle: A Life in Science', Aurum (2005) p. 261
6 ADS 1994ARA&A..32....1B
7 *Nature*, vol. 232, p. 289 (1971)
8 *Nature*, vol. 239, p. 117 (1972)

9 *The Times*, 11 Sept. 1972, p. 2
10 *Nature*, vol. 239, p. 121 (1972)
11 National Archives, CAB 164/1335
12 *The Times*, 15 Jan. 1973, p. 2
13 *The Times*, 31 Jan. 1973, p. 15
14 *The Times*, 24 Feb. 1973, p. 13
15 *The Times*, 27 Feb. 1973, p. 15
16 *The Times*, 3 April 1973, p. 15
17 ADS 1945Obs....66..153R
18 Ibid.
19 Hoyle, F., 'Home is where the wind blows', Oxford University Press (1997), p. 317
20 *Social Studies of Science*, vol 13, pp. 161-2 (1983)
21 *Social Studies of Science*, vol 13, pp. 49-86 (1983)
22 *Quarterly Journal of the Royal Astronomical Society*, vol 3, pp. 249-58, (1962)
23 *Nature*, vol 301, p. 561 (1983)
24 *Social Studies of Science*, vol 13, pp. 161-2 (1983)

Chapter 8 (pages 96-106)

1 *Nature*, vol 255, pp. 581-3 (1975)
2 Newton, I,. 'Opticks', Dover Publications edition (1952), p. III
3 Piazzi Smyth, C., 'Teneriffe, an astronomer's experiment' London: Lovell Reeve, 1858, p. viii
4 RGO 11/1: Alexander, J.B., memo, 23 April 1971
5 Letter from H.H. Atkinson to F.C.O., 26 June 1973, National Archives CAB 164/1335
6 http://www.ing.iac.es/PR/tour/rein2.html
7 ADS 1976Obs....96...83.

Chapter 9 (pages 107-120)

1 www.ing.iac.es/PR/tour/murdin.pdf
2 RGO 19/2/4: *Gemini*, No. 11 (July 1984)
3 RGO 19/2/4: *Gemini*, No. 13 (February 1985)
4 ADS 1995IrAJ...22..216.
5 www.cosmotography.com/images/canary_island_adventure_1.html
6 *The Times*, 1 July 1985, p. 4

Chapter 10 (pages 121-137)

1 ADS 1984MNRAS.211P..33P
2 www.ing.iac.es/PR/SH/SH93/high_93.html, and references given there
3 www.ing.iac.es/PR/SH/SH94/high_94.html

4 www.ing.iac.es/PR/SH/SH2005/ di.html and www.ing.iac.es/PR/ newsletter/news10/science3.html
5 www.ing.iac.es/PR/SH/SH95/ high_95.html, and www.ing.iac.es/ PR/AR1997/high_97.htm
6 ADS 1994MNRAS.271L...5C, and preceding parts linked from there.
7 ADS 2005MNRAS.359.1096B
8 www.superwasp.org
9 www.ing.iac.es/PR/SH/SH2005/ iphas.html

10 http://de.arxiv.org/PS_cache/ arxiv/pdf/0801/0801.2186v3.pdf
11 RGO 19/2/4: *Gemini*, No. 30, pp. 6-8 (1990)
12 www.ing.iac.es/PR/AR1998/ high_98.html
13 www.ing.iac.es/PR/AR1997/ high_97.htm
14 ADS 1991MNRAS.249..498M ; ADS 1995MNRAS.273..257M
15 ADS 1994MNRAS.266L..27L
16 ADS 1995ApJ...440L..41P

17 http://arxiv.org/PS_cache/astro- ph/pdf/9602/9602122v1.pdf
18 ADS 1999ApJ...517..565P

Epilogue (pages 138-142)

1 www.herstmonceux-castle.com
2 www.the-observatory.org
3 www.ing.iac.es/PR/newsletter/ news5/ins1.pdf
4 ADS 1991JBAA..101..111G
5 Méndez Alvarez, J., e-mail to the author

Picture credits

Images prefixed CUL are reproduced by permission of the Syndics of Cambridge University Library.
Images prefixed ING are reproduced by courtesy of the Isaac Newton Group of Telescopes, La Palma.
Images prefixed OSC are from archive material held by the Observatory Science Centre, Herstmonceux.
Photographs and diagrams not listed below are the author's own.

Cover *background:* ING/F. Vilardell, I. Ribas and C. Jordi, N. Szymanek
   inset: ING/RGO
p 9   *bottom:* ING/Nik Szymanek
p 10 CUL RGO118/9664
p 13 CUL RGO118/ 8457
p 14 Carnegie Observatories photographic Collection, The Huntington Library, San Marino.
p 15 E7910 © National Maritime Museum, Greenwich
p 18 Out-of-copyright image from Newton, 'Principia',1803 ed., http://books.google.co.uk/ books?id=gi5WAAAAMAAJ
p 21 Out-of-copyright image (1867) from Wikimedia Commons
p 22 Out-of-copyright image (1860) from Wikimedia Commons
p 23 OSC
p 24 *top:* OSC
   inset: Brian Mack
   bottom: CUL RGO118/14664
p 26 OSC E26625
p 27 OSC YIP554
p 32 Corning Incorporated, Archives
p 36 *top:* Bentley Historical Library, University of Michigan
   bottom: Out-of-copyright image (1896) from Wikimedia Commons
p 38 OSC
p 40 *both:* by courtesy of Optical Science Laboratory, University College London
p 44 ROG2851 © National Maritime Museum, Greenwich
p 47 *aerial view:* © Google Earth
p 49 CUL RGO118/9429
p 51 *top:* CUL RGO118/12940
p 53 OSC/*Eastbourne Argus*
p 55 *top:* OSC

p 58 Out-of-copyright image from Nasmyth, 'Autobiography', 1905 ed., http://www. archive.org/details/ jamesnasengineer00nasmrich
p 59 ING/George Nicholson
p 60 *bottom:* CUL RGO118/1955
p 61 OSC
p 62 CUL RGO118/8475
p 63 OSC
p 64 ING/RGO
p 65 adapted from *The Engineer*, 1967
p 66 CUL RGO118/3038-15
p 69 OSC P546
p 71 adapted from ADS 1975MNRAS .172..289B, p.293, by permission of Wiley-Blackwell
p 72 CUL RGO118/11761
p 74 OSC P971
p 75 NASA image (adapted)
p 77 OSC P352
p 80 OSC P748
p 83 OSC, reproduced by permission of Mrs Jill Wallis
p 84 CUL RGO118/13619/1
p 86 *Nature*, vol. 239, p.121, 1972
p 87 OSC
p 92 OSC
p 93 *top left:* CUL RGO118/12979, *bottom:* OSC
p 94 CUL RGO118/13864
p 95 ING/Nik Szymanek
p 99 Out-of-copyright image from Piazzi Smyth, 'Teneriffe ...', 1858, http:// books.google.co.uk/ books?id=TmsPAAAAYAAJ
p 100 *base map:* Wikimedia Commons
p 101 NASA/World Wind
p 102 Hubertus Wöhl, http://www3. kis.uni-freiburg.de/~hw/ sitetesting.html
p 105 *both:* ING/Rein Bakker
p 107 ING/RGO
p 108 CUL RGO118/13865

p 109 ING/Peter Sorensen and Nik Szymanek
p 110 *top:* ING/Jens Moser
p 111 ING/Grubb Parsons
p 112 *top:* ING/Simon Tulloch
   inset: ING/Romano Corradi
p 113 ING/RGO; *inset:* ING
p 114 ING/B. W. Hadley
p 116 ING/RGO
p 118 ING/Nik Szymanek
p 119 ING/Simon Driver (St Andrews University)
p 120 *top:* ING
p 122 ING/Simon Dye (Cardiff University)
p 123 ING/Alan Fitzsimmons (Queen's University, Belfast)
p 124 ING/Alan Fitzsimmons (Queen's University, Belfast)
p 125 ING/Stephen Lowry (Queen's University Belfast)
p 128 ING/S. Hughes and S. Maddox (Institute of Astronomy, Cambridge)
p 129 ING/Nick Wright) University College London) on behalf of the IPHAS collaboration
p 130 *top:* ING/Jonathan Irwin (Institute of Astronomy, Cambridge)/IPHAS; middle: ING/Nick Wright and the IPHAS collaboration
   bottom: ING/Romano Corradi
p 131 ING/Isobel Hook (University of California, Berkeley)
p 134 ING/Tom Shanks (University of Durham)
p 134 ING/RGO
p 137 ING/Javier Méndez (ING), Pilar Ruiz-Lapuente (University of Barcelona) and Nic Walton (ING)
p 141 *middle:* OSC P546
   bottom: ING/Javier Méndez (ING) and Nik Szymanek
p 148 ING/R. Barrena and D. López (IAC)

Index

Stellar birthplace: regions of intense star-formation show up red in this colour-filtered image of the 'Pinwheel' Galaxy (M101) obtained with the Wide Field Camera on the Isaac Newton Telescope on La Palma in 2009.